11+ Mixed Workouts

For the **CEM** test

These brilliant CGP 10-Minute Workouts will test children on a mixture of Maths, Verbal Reasoning and Non-Verbal Reasoning skills. Perfect for making sure they can confidently swap between subjects in the real CEM 11+ test.

We've also included step-by-step answers, along with a helpful progress chart.

This is Book 1. You'll find more Mixed Workouts at the same level in Book 2!

10-Minute Tests

Ages
10-11

How to access your free Online Edition

This book includes a free Online Edition to read on your PC, Mac or tablet.
You'll just need to go to **cgpbooks.co.uk/extras** and enter this code:

4153 1766 2815 8871

By the way, this code only works for one person. If somebody else has used this book before you, they might have already claimed the Online Edition.

How to use this book

This book is made up of 10-minute workouts and puzzle pages.
There are answers and detailed explanations in the pull-out section at the back of the book.

10-Minute Workouts

- There are 30 workouts in this book, each containing two different subjects from
  Maths, Verbal Reasoning, Comprehension and Non-Verbal Reasoning.

- Each workout is designed to focus on questions that your child could come across in their
  11+ Test. They cover a variety of skills and techniques at the right difficulty levels.

- If your child hasn't managed to finish the workout in time, they need to work on increasing their
  speed, whereas if they have made a lot of mistakes, they need to work more carefully.

- Keep track of your child's scores using the progress chart on the inside back cover of the book.

Puzzle Pages

- There are 9 puzzle pages in this book, which are a great break from test-style questions.
  They encourage children to practise the same skills that they will need in the test, but in
  a fun way.

Published by CGP

Editors:
Luke Bennett, Tom Carney, Emma Clayton, Emma Cleasby, Alex Fairer, Katherine Faudemer, Sophie Herring,
Hannah Roscoe, Ben Train

With thanks to Will Garrison, Alison Griffin, Sharon Keeley-Holden, David Ryan
and Karen Wells for the proofreading.

Please note that CGP is not associated with CEM or The University of Durham in any way.
This book does not include any official questions and it is not endorsed by CEM or The University of Durham.

CEM, Centre for Evaluation and Monitoring, Durham University and *The University of Durham*
are all trademarks of The University of Durham.

ISBN: 978 1 78908 201 2
Printed by Elanders Ltd, Newcastle upon Tyne
Clipart from Corel®

Based on the classic CGP style created by Richard Parsons.

Contents

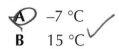

Workout 1

Q1-7 will test your **maths** skills.
You have **6 minutes** to complete Q1-7.

1. Yesterday the temperature was 4 °C. Today it is 11 degrees colder.
    What is the temperature today? Circle the correct option.

    A –7 °C ✓   **C** 7 °C   **E** –6 °C
    B 15 °C ✓   **D** –5 °C

2. Eduardo puts a cake in the oven at 13:37, for 35 minutes. What time does
    Eduardo take the cake out of the oven? Give your answer in 24-hour clock format.

    13:37
    + 35
    ─────
    13:72
    14:12

    13:37   1 4 : 1 2 ✓
    – 35
    13:72   14:12

3. The graph below shows a quadrilateral.

    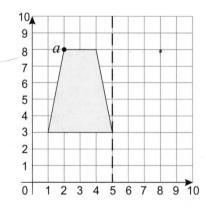

    If the shape is reflected along the dotted line what will the coordinates
    of point *a* of the new reflected shape be?

    (8 , 8) ✓

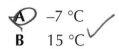

4. What is the next number in the sequence below? Circle the correct option.

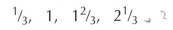

$\frac{1}{3}$, 1, $1\frac{2}{3}$, $2\frac{1}{3}$ ⌣ 2

A $2\frac{2}{3}$ **C** 3   E 4

B $3\frac{1}{3}$ D $3\frac{2}{3}$ ✓

5. If there are 21 weekdays in April this year, what percentage of April's days are weekdays?

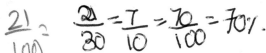

$\frac{21}{100}$ $\frac{21}{30} = \frac{7}{10} = \frac{70}{100} = 70\%$.

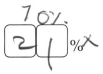

7 0%.

⬚⬚ % ✗

6. Franklin has 5 m of ribbon that he uses to wrap 5 small presents and 3 large presents. He works out that he needs 50 cm for each small present and 80 cm for each large present. How much ribbon will he have left over?

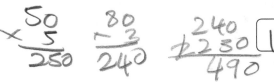

$\begin{array}{r} 50 \\ \times 5 \\ \hline 250 \end{array}$ $\begin{array}{r} 80 \\ \times 3 \\ \hline 240 \end{array}$ $\begin{array}{r} 240 \\ +250 \\ \hline 490 \end{array}$ ✓   ⬚1⬚0⬚ cm

7. A regular hexagon is shown below. *O* is its centre point.

$\begin{array}{r} 4\,|\,6 \\ \times\,72 \\ \hline 32 \\ 120 \\ \hline 15 \end{array}$

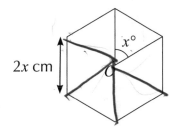

2x cm $x°$ *O*

not drawn accurately

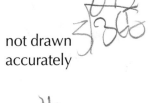

$\begin{array}{r} 072 \\ 3\,\overline{)360} \end{array}$

16

What is the perimeter of the shape? Circle the correct option.

A 5.4 m   **C** 600 cm   **E** 7.2 m

B 3.6 m   D 120 cm

3

Work out which of the options best fits in place of the missing hexagon in the grid.

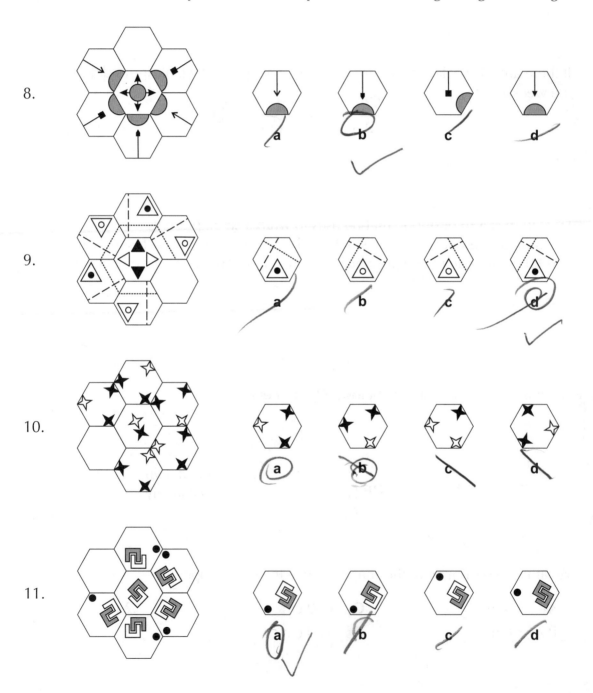

8.

    a   b   c   d

9.

    a   b   c   d

10.

    a   b   c   d

11.

    a   b   c   d

Work out which option is a top-down 2D view of the 3D figure on the left.

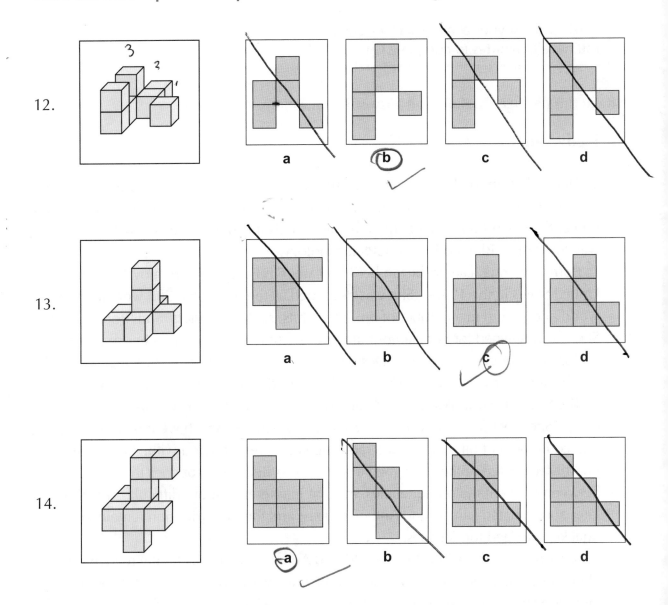

12.   a   b ✓   c   d

13.   a   b   c ✓   d

14.   a ✓   b   c   d

5

/ 14

Q1-7 will test your **comprehension** skills.
You have **6 minutes** to complete Q1-7.

Read this passage carefully and answer the questions that follow.

Hedy Lamarr

During her unusual career, Hedy Lamarr was involved in the glamorous world of Hollywood films, and she also made significant contributions to science. She became one of the biggest film stars of her time, as well as inventing a device that paved the way for Wi-Fi®, Bluetooth® and GPS technology.

5   Born in Vienna, Lamarr began her film career in Europe before moving to the United States in the 1930s. She was described as the most beautiful woman in the world and starred in a number of box-office hits, such as 'Algiers' and 'Boom Town'. She was renowned for her glamour and looks, but few knew that in her spare time she nurtured an interest in science. Despite a lack of formal scientific training, she studied
10 and became knowledgeable about aviation, aerodynamics and military technology.

    The Second World War spurred Lamarr to use her talents to contribute to the war effort. She identified a flaw in the US Navy's torpedoes, which were radio-controlled and could be sent off course if the radio signals were interfered with. Lamarr and her friend George Antheil designed a guidance system for torpedoes that would 'hop'
15 between different radio frequencies, making interference more difficult. The Navy later appropriated Lamarr and Antheil's ideas, and their contribution remained unacknowledged for decades.

    It wasn't until the 1990s that Lamarr and Antheil's work was finally recognised. Then in her eighties, Lamarr was honoured with awards by the scientific community.
20 Her pioneering work in radio communication is the basis for the wireless transmission technologies that are so commonly used today.

Answer these questions about the text that you've just read.
Circle the letter that matches the correct answer.

1. According to the text, which of the following statements about Lamarr must be false?

   A   She had a wide variety of talents.

   B   She worked internationally as an actress.

   C   She invented Bluetooth® technology.

   D   She was well-regarded for her on-screen career.

2. Which of the following best describes what people thought about Lamarr during her film career?

   A   She was considered the best actress of her generation.

   B   She was famed for her beauty.

   C   She was considered eccentric because of her inventions.

   D   She was considered an expert in aviation.

3. According to the text, which of the following statements about Lamarr must be true?

   A   She was an experienced pilot.

   B   She taught herself about science.

   C   She moved to Algiers, Algeria.

   D   She believed beauty was more important than intelligence.

4. What did Lamarr do during the Second World War?

   A   She worked for the US government to help the war effort.

   B   She built torpedoes for the US Navy.

   C   She criticised the war effort.

   D   She worked to improve existing American weaponry.

5. According to the text, what was the problem with the Navy's torpedoes?

   A   They were controlled by weak radio signals.

   B   They interfered with other pieces of equipment.

   C   Enemy forces could send them astray.

   D   They didn't have enough power to get to their destination.

6. Why was Lamarr's work with torpedoes not recognised at first?

   A   The US Navy used Lamarr's work but didn't credit her.

   B   She wanted to be known only for her film career.

   C   No one believed she was capable of inventing anything.

   D   George Antheil got all of the credit.

7. Why was Lamarr given awards in the 1990s?

   A   For inventing many of today's wireless technologies.

   B   For continuing to make inventions well into her eighties.

   C   For her work in radio communication technology.

   D   For her contribution to the film industry.

Q8-12 will test your **maths** skills.
You have **4 minutes** to complete Q8-12.

8. How many lines of symmetry does the following shape have?
   Circle the correct option.

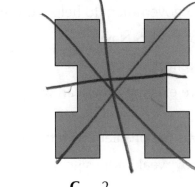

   A   0   **C**   2   **E**   8
   B   1   **D**   4

9. What is $6^2 \times (72 - 68)$?

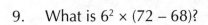

10. Work out the area of the shape below.

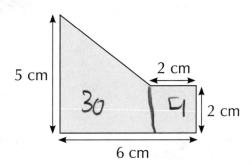

5 cm

2 cm

30

4

2 cm

6 cm

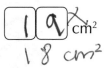

1 8 cm²

Look at the diagram below.

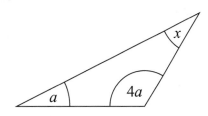

x

$4a$

a

11 Which of the following equations is correct? Circle the correct option.

A $x = 2a - 180$ C $x = 180 - 5a$ E $x + 4a = 180$

B $90 - 4a = a$ D $4a = 270$

12. If $a = 30°$, what is the value of x?

1 8 0
− 1 6 0
1 2 0

/ 12

These puzzles are a great way to practise your **matching** and **word-unscrambling** skills.

Alien Antics

Garry the alien is working undercover on Planet Zog. He needs a disguise that will make him look as similar as possible to the local aliens. Which outfit should he choose?

Local aliens

Cooking Crisis

Paula is making a three-course meal, but she's forgotten some of the ingredients. Unscramble the anagrams below to work out what the forgotten ingredients are. The name of a final ingredient is also hidden in the words below. Unscramble the highlighted letters to work out what it is.

SNIRPAPS

_ _ ☐ _ _ _ _ _

MOOTATES

_ _ _ ☐ _ _ _ _

SARCUTD

_ _ _ ☐ _ ☐ _

ROGANES

☐ _ _ _ _ _ _

GILCAR

_ _ _ _ _ ☐

CIBUISST

_ _ _ _ _ ☐ _ _

The final ingredient is _____ .

Q1-11 will test your **non-verbal reasoning** skills.
You have **6 minutes** to complete Q1-11.

Look at how the first two figures are changed, and then work out which option would look like the third figure if you changed it in the same way.

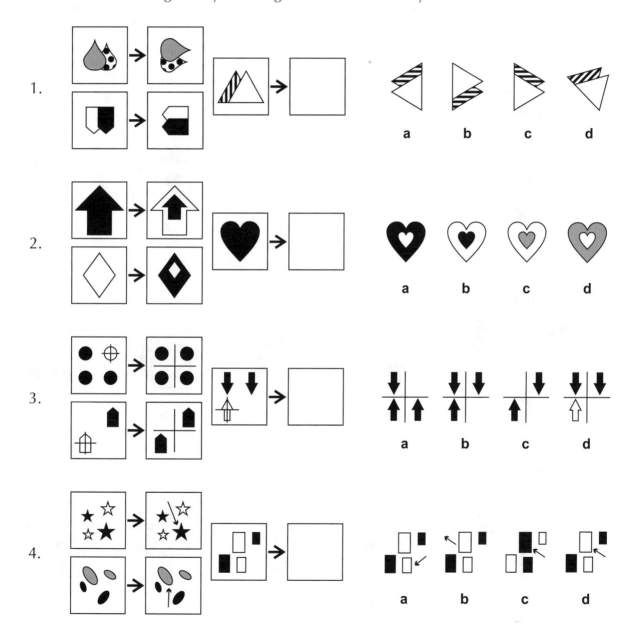

Work out which of the four cubes can be made from the net.

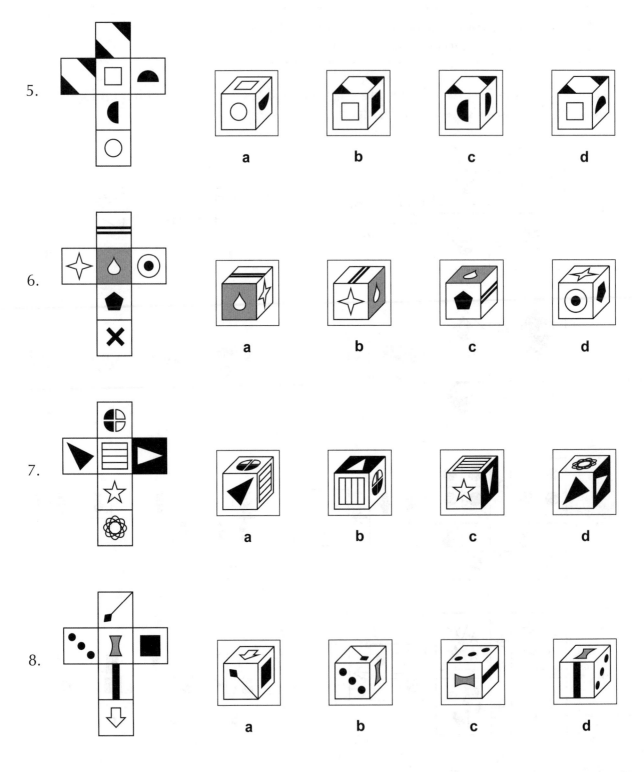

5.

a   b   c   d

6.

a   b   c   d

7.

a   b   c   d

8.

a   b   c   d

Work out which of the options best fits in place of the missing square in the grid.

9.

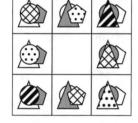

a   b   c   d   e

10.

a   b   c   d   e

11.

a   b   c   d   e

In each question below, the words can be rearranged to form a sentence.
One word doesn't fit in the sentence. Underline the word that doesn't fit.

Example: red   the   has   <u>ride</u>   girl   bicycle   a

12.   obtain   licence   before   a   in   must   you   to   cars   drive   order

13.   storm   went   got   and   exercise   a   in   caught   out   walking   we

14.   working   arrived   several   fix   bathroom   to   plumbers   flooded   the

15.   wearing   red   ball   not   did   Chuckles   his   nose   clown   the   like

16.   sheep   a   fence   slip   in   allowed   my   escape   to   hole   three

17.   in   carrots   eating   helps   the   dark   to   vision   you   see

Find the word that means the opposite, or nearly the opposite,
of the word on the left.

Example: **first**   later   <u>last</u>   next   beginning

18.   **arid**   moist   sharp   frosty   misty

19.   **calm**   dormant   acrid   flustered   sullen

20.   **increase**   languish   wane   dim   slacken

21.   **honesty**   stealth   slander   betrayal   deceit

22.   **depression**   relief   euphoria   frenzy   keenness

23.   **selfish**   amiable   pompous   tolerant   altruistic

/ 23

Q1-11 will test your **non-verbal reasoning** skills.
You have **6 minutes** to complete Q1-11.

Work out which option would look like the figure on the left if it was rotated.

1. **Rotate**

                      a   b   c   d

2. **Rotate**

                      a   b   c   d

3. **Rotate**

                      a   b   c   d

4. **Rotate**

                      a   b   c   d

5. **Rotate**

                      a   b   c   d

Workout 4

Work out which option is most like the two figures on the left.

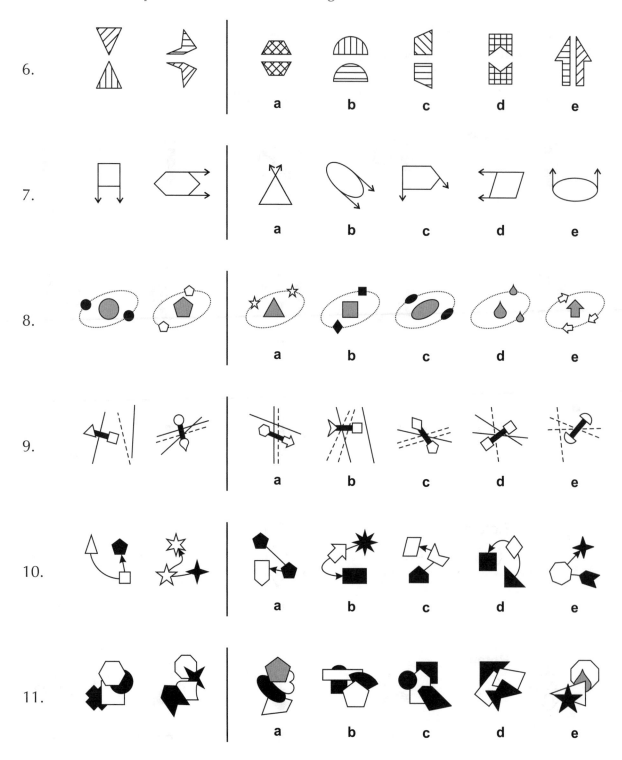

12. The population of a town is 56 713. Round the population to the nearest thousand.

13. Next year 2824 people will move out of the town. What will the population of the town be after the people leave?

14. The nth term of a sequence is $3(n + 5)$. What is the 18th term of the sequence?

   A   59   **C**   33   **E**   26

   B   72   **D**   69

15. A shop sells 4 different colours of pencil case. The pie chart shows how many pencil cases of each colour were sold last month. They sold 216 pencil cases in total.

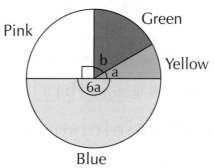

   Half the pencil cases sold were blue. How many green pencil cases were sold?

/ 15

Fill in the missing letters to complete the words in the following passage.

1. The city of Venice is renowned for its `t__di_i_n` of masks.

2. Popular with today's tourists as `__uv_ni_s`, they are widely

3. `a__oc__ted` with the Carnival of Venice — this annual

4. festival provides an `_pp___u__ty` for revellers to dress up

5. and disguise themselves. Some masks are `_rn_t__l_` decorated

6. with jewels and feathers, while others are a `_ta_k` white. Some conceal

   the wearer's whole face, while others only cover the eyes. One of the most iconic

7. masks is the `_in_st_r` *Medico della peste*, which has a long,

   curved beak. This mask wasn't originally a part of the carnival celebrations,

8. but rather a protective `m_a_u_e` taken by plague doctors in the

9. 17th century. Sweet-smelling `s_bs__nc__` such as flowers

10. were `_o_ta_ned` within the beak, as at the time it was believed

    that foul smells were responsible for spreading infection.

Work out which of the options best fits in place of the missing hexagon in the grid.

11.

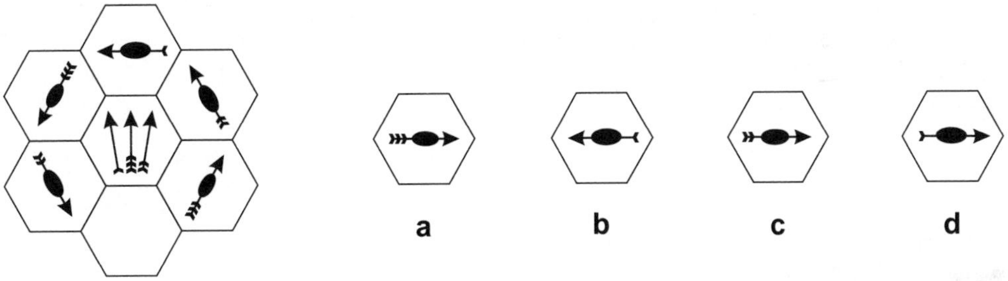

a b c d

12.

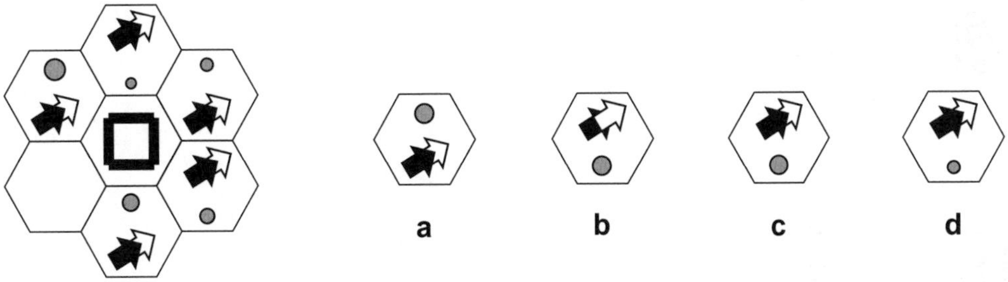

a b c d

13.

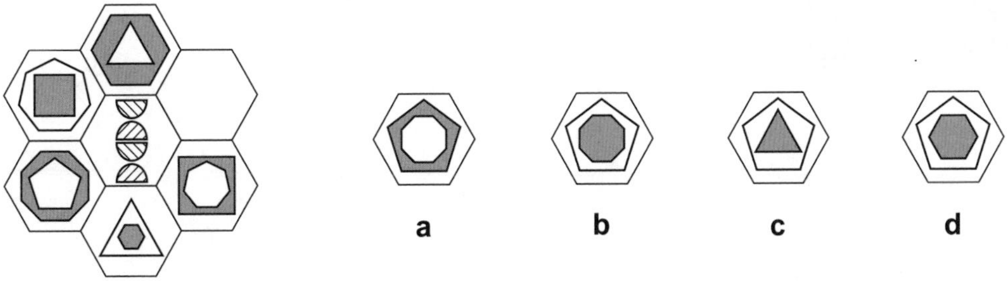

a b c d

Look at how the first two figures are changed, and then work out which option would look like the third figure if you changed it in the same way.

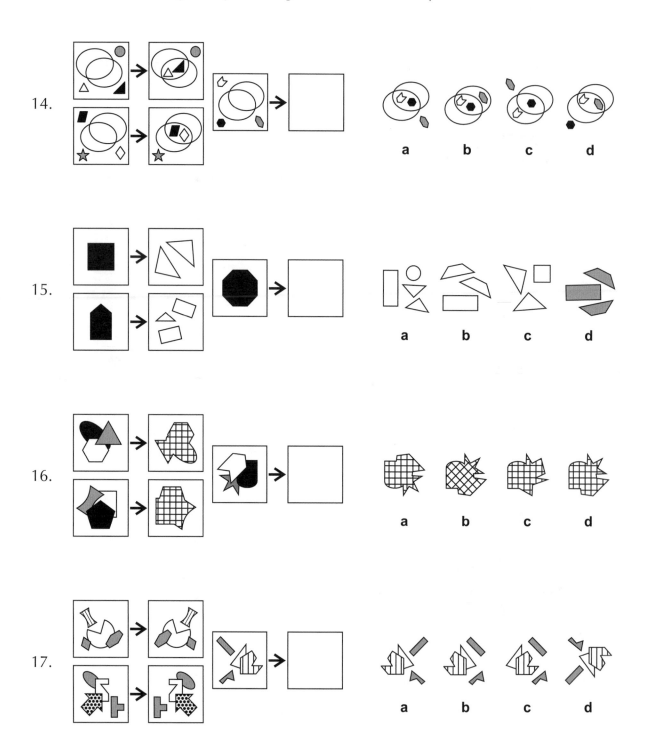

14.

a   b   c   d

15.

a   b   c   d

16.

a   b   c   d

17.

a   b   c   d

Work out which set of blocks can be put together to make the 3D figure on the left.

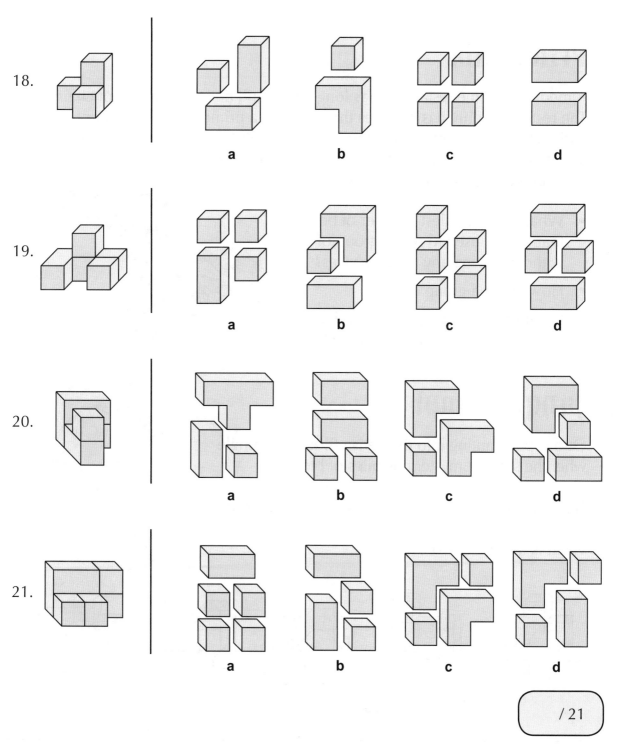

18.

a

b

c

d

19.

a

b

c

d

20.

a

b

c

d

21.

a

b

c

d

/ 21

Workout 5

These puzzles are a fun way to practise with **prime numbers** and **3D views**.

Prime Ribs

A medieval theme restaurant has long tables and benches instead of chairs. The restaurant only has benches that can seat a prime number of people and no bench can seat more than 10 people. But the staff say they can use their benches to seat groups of customers of any size without leaving any spaces on the benches.

- What is the smallest number of benches that can be used to seat a group of 11, without leaving any empty spaces?

- How about a group of 18?

- What's the smallest group size that would need more than four benches?

Jungle Jump!

Otto is parachuting into the dense Blockadia jungle when he see five mysterious piles of blocks.

From above, the dark blue blocks spell out a word.

What is the secret word?

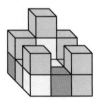 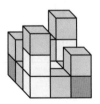 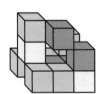 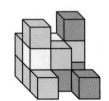 

22

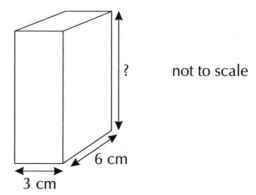
Q1-5 will test your **maths** skills.
You have **4 minutes** to complete Q1-5.

Below is part of a timetable for the X2 bus.

Stop	Hallow	Wilt	Clawson	Bardgrove
Time	11:54	12:27	12:46	13:08

1.   How long does the bus take to get from Hallow to Bardgrove?

⬚⬚ minutes

2.   Give the shortest time the bus travels between two stops. Circle the correct option.

    A   22 minutes   **C**   13 minutes   **E**   33 minutes

    B   9 minutes   **D**   19 minutes

3.   One week Ruben earns £240. He spends 20% of the money on bike accessories.
      How much does Ruben have left? Circle the correct option.

    A   £200   **C**   £172   **E**   £168

    B   £192   **D**   £180

4.   The volume of the cuboid below is 144 cm³. What is the height of the cuboid?

?

not to scale

6 cm

3 cm

⬚ cm

23

5. Alessandro recorded the number of cars that passed his house everyday between 1 pm and 2 pm in a bar chart.

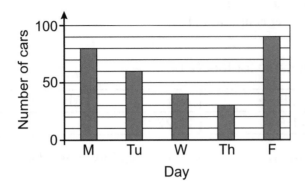

Work out the mean number of cars that passed Alessandro's house every minute during the time he was recording.

Q6-23 will test your **verbal reasoning** skills.
You have **6 minutes** to complete Q6-23.

Three of the words in each list are linked. Mark the word that is not related to these three.

Example: journal   diary   <u>textbook</u>   notebook

6. glow   bright   glare   shine

7. hammer   mallet   beat   pound

8. report   fax   text   email

9. drain   milk   water   bleed

10. feline   bovine   canine   alpine

Mark the word outside the brackets that has a similar meaning to the words in both sets of brackets.

Example: (twig branch) (fasten attach)   glue <u>stick</u> affix bough

11. (trail way)   (shadow stalk)   seek capture tail track

12. (dismal gloomy)   (evil black)   dim sinful dark unlit

13. (convoy caravan)   (school educate)   train practice retinue drill

14. (decelerate brake) (leisurely unhurried) lagged creep slow suspend

15. (realise recognise) (value prize)   fathom espy appreciate extol

16. (dear intimate)   (finish end)   close goal expire fast

Complete the word on the right so that it means the same, or nearly the same, as the word on the left.

Example: scared | a | f | r | a | i | d |

17. unexciting | m | | n | | | n | e |

18. question | i | | t | e | | r | o | | a | | e |

19. thankfulness | | r | a | | i | t | | | e |

20. dismissal | | | j | e | | t | i | | n |

21. determined | r | | s | | l | u | | e |

22. indispensable | e | | s | | n | | i | a | |

23. satisfactory | | d | | q | | | t | e |

/ 23

Workout 6

Q1-7 will test your **comprehension** skills.
You have **6 minutes** to complete Q1-7.

Read this passage carefully and answer the questions that follow.

An adapted extract from 'Moby Dick'

I had not been seated very long ere* a man of a certain venerable robustness entered; immediately as the storm-pelted door flew back upon admitting him, a quick regardful eyeing of him by all the congregation, sufficiently attested that this fine old man was the chaplain**. Yes, it was the famous Father Mapple, so called by
5   the whalemen, among whom he was a very great favourite. He had been a sailor and a harpooneer*** in his youth, but for many years past had dedicated his life to the Church. When he entered I observed that he carried no umbrella, and certainly had not come in his carriage, for his tarpaulin hat ran down with melting sleet, and his great pilot cloth jacket seemed almost to drag him to the floor with the weight of
10   the water it had absorbed. However, hat and coat and overshoes were one by one removed, and hung up in a little space in an adjacent corner; when, arrayed in a decent suit, he quietly approached the pulpit.
Like most old fashioned pulpits, it was a very lofty one, and since a regular stairs to such a height would seriously contract the already small area of the chapel, the
15   architect, it seemed, had acted upon the hint of Father Mapple, and finished the pulpit without a stairs, substituting a perpendicular side ladder, like those used in mounting a ship from a boat at sea. Halting for an instant at the foot of the ladder, Father Mapple cast a look upwards, and then with a truly sailor-like but still reverential dexterity, hand over hand, mounted the steps as if ascending the main-top**** of his vessel.

Hermann Melville

* ere — *before*
** chaplain — *minister of religion*
*** harpooneer — *someone who uses a harpoon (a type of spear)*
**** main-top — *platform on a ship's mainmast*

Answer these questions about the text that you've just read.
Circle the letter that matches the correct answer.

1. Which of the following best describes the state of the chapel door in line 2?

   A   It has been destroyed by the storm.

   B   It has been soaked by rain from the storm.

   C   It has been blown open by the storm.

   D   It has a special coating on it to protect it from the storm.

2. How does the narrator quickly determine that the old man entering the chapel is Father Mapple?

   A   The narrator has met Father Mapple before.

   B   The old man is dressed like a chaplain.

   C   He notices that the congregation respect the old man.

   D   The members of the congregation greet Father Mapple by name.

3. Which of the following statements about Father Mapple is true?

   A   He has only recently become a chaplain.

   B   He has been a chaplain for a long time.

   C   He is still a sailor.

   D   He has recently retired from working as a sailor.

4. Why does the narrator believe that Father Mapple didn't come to the chapel in a carriage?

   A   He notices that Father Mapple has an umbrella.

   B   He knows that Father Mapple doesn't own a carriage.

   C   He sees that Father Mapple's clothes are completely drenched.

   D   He realises that Father Mapple's shoes are covered in mud.

5. What does the word "lofty" (line 13) mean?

   A   Elevated   **C**   Modest

   B   Opulent   **D**   Spacious

6. Why does the pulpit have a ladder rather than stairs?

    A   The architect thought it would look better.

    B   Stairs were too expensive to build.

    C   All old-fashioned pulpits have ladders.

    D   A ladder takes up less space than stairs.

7. Which of the following best describes Father Mapple as he climbs up the pulpit?

    A   Nimble and dignified

    B   Speedy and boisterous

    C   Slow and laboured

    D   Apprehensive and serious

> Q8-14 will test your **non-verbal reasoning** skills.
> You have **4 minutes** to complete Q8-14.

Work out which of the options best fits in place of the missing square in the series.

8.
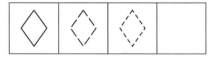

                                            a   **b**   **c**   **d**

9.
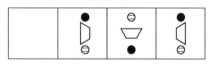

                                            a   **b**   **c**   **d**

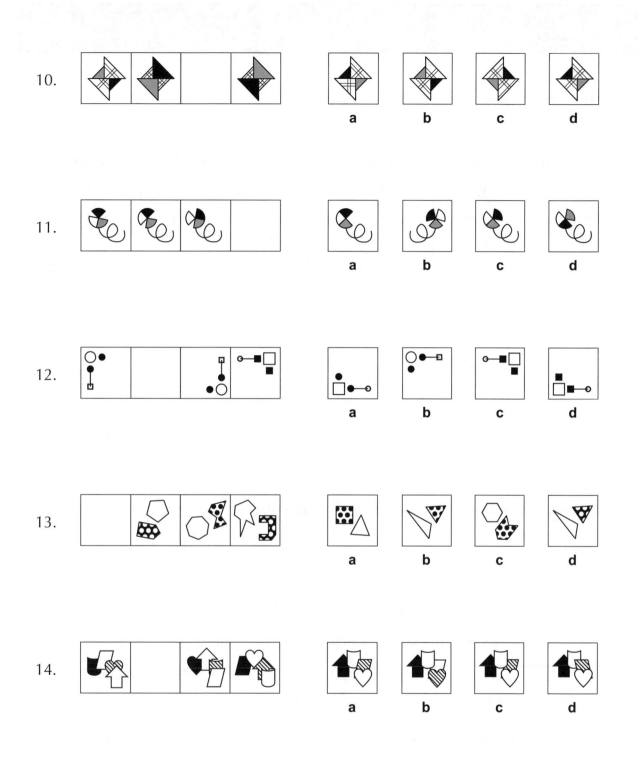

10.

11.

12.

13.

14.

/ 14

29

Q1-5 will test your **maths** skills.
You have **4 minutes** to complete Q1-5.

1. Which of the following nets makes a pentagonal prism? Circle the correct option.

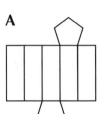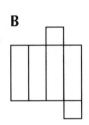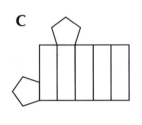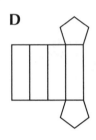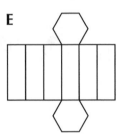

The heights of five sunflowers in Yvonne's garden are:

120 cm, 0.9 m, 1.15 m, 1.85 m, 90 cm

2. What is the difference between the 2nd tallest and 3rd tallest sunflower?

 cm

3. Work out the mean height of Yvonne's sunflowers.

 m

Rohima is running in a 3.5 km race. She is 780 m from the finishing line.

4. How far has Rohima run so far? Circle the correct option.

    A   2.2 km   **C**   2.68 km   **E**   2.84 km

    B   2.52 km   **D**   2.72 km

5. Rohima jogs the last 780 m to the finish line, at a speed of 4 m per second.
    How long will it take her to reach the finish line?

    minutes   seconds

Q6-16 will test your **non-verbal reasoning** skills.
You have **6 minutes** to complete Q6-16.

Work out which 3D figure in the grey box has been rotated to make the new 3D figure.

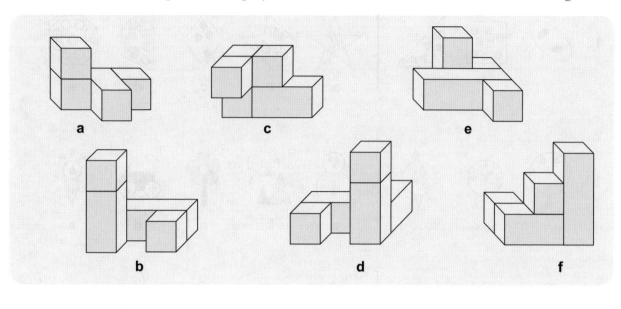

6.
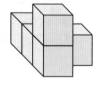

a   d

b   e

c   f

7.
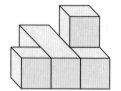

a   d

b   e

c   f

8.
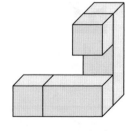

a   d

b   e

c   f

9.
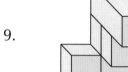

a   d

b   e

c   f

10.
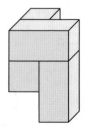

a   d

b   e

c   f

11.
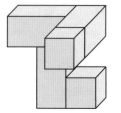

a   d

b   e

c   f

Workout 8

Work out which option is most like the three figures on the left.

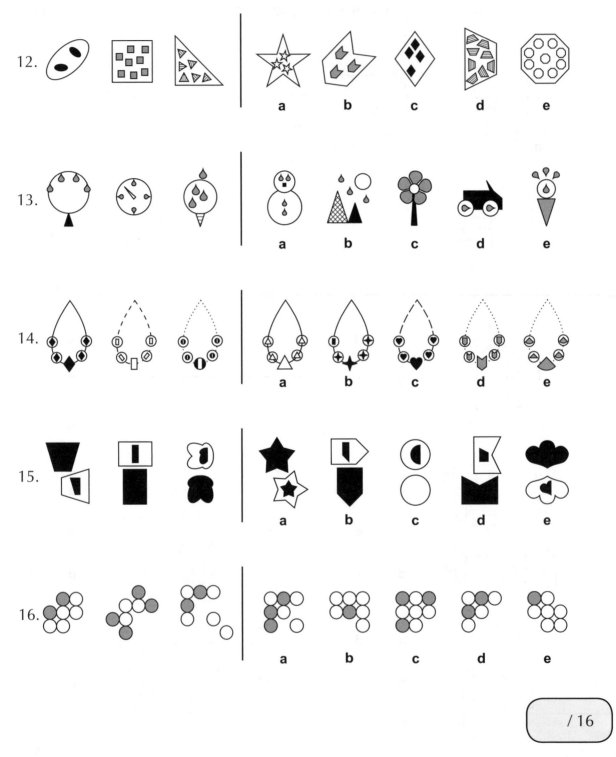

/ 16

Have a go at these puzzles for a fun way to practise **maths reasoning** and **antonyms**.

Scaly Surprise

Harriet works in a zoo. A crocodile egg has been accidentally mixed up with five penguin eggs. Harriet needs to find which is the crocodile egg before it hatches. She can't tell by looking but she knows all the penguin eggs weigh exactly the same and the crocodile egg is a little bit heavier. She decides to use balance scales to find the crocodile egg.

What is the fewest number of times Harriet needs to use the scales to be sure of finding the crocodile egg?

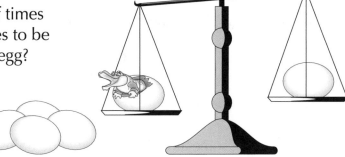

Antonym Actions

Complete the wordsearch by finding an **antonym** for each of the verbs below. Write each antonym on the correct line. The first letter of each antonym has been done for you.

resist	s_____
divide	c_____
continue	q_____
facilitate	o_____
expand	s_____
clean	s_____
heed	i_____

E	S	H	R	I	N	K	T	I	B
H	L	O	P	T	Q	C	M	W	A
S	A	H	I	D	U	S	H	K	E
T	S	U	R	R	E	N	D	E	R
A	Q	D	T	A	V	F	R	C	O
I	O	S	Y	E	G	I	R	J	N
N	B	E	N	I	B	M	O	C	G
O	G	A	X	K	L	S	P	D	I

Q1-8 will test your **maths** skills.
You have **6 minutes** to complete Q1-8.

1. The ages of children in an activity club are: 6, 7, 6, 5, 8, 6, 7, 7, 8, 4, 5, 7.
    What is the most common age in the club?

2. What is $\frac{1}{4} + \frac{3}{8}$? Circle the correct option.

    A $\frac{5}{8}$ **C** $\frac{4}{32}$ **E** $\frac{1}{2}$

    B $\frac{2}{8}$ **D** $\frac{4}{4}$

3. Amber is doing some athletics training. She trains by sprinting 115 m and then
    resting before sprinting again. She sprints 7 times. How far does she run in total?
    Circle the correct option.

    A 735 m   **C** 775 m   **E** 480 m

    B 625 m   **D** 805 m

4. Two regular pentagons are shown in the
    diagram below. What is the value of *x*?

    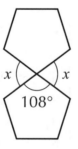

5.   If $y = 52 \div 13$, what is y^3? Circle the correct option.

    A   64   **C**   124   **E**   48

    B   27   **D**   16

The pictogram shows the number of cars that started and finished three motor races.

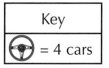

Race 1	Started	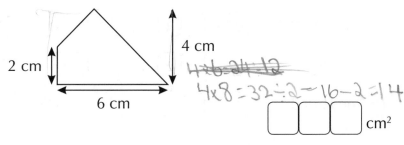
	Finished	
Race 2	Started	
	Finished	
Race 3	Started	
	Finished	

Key
= 4 cars

6.   What is the mean number of cars that started the three races?

7.   What percentage of the cars that started Race 2 finished it?

    %

8.   A triangle with an 8 cm base had a smaller triangle cut off one corner.
    The new shape now has a 6 cm base and is shown below.
    Work out the area of the new shape.

2 cm   4 cm

6 cm

$4+6=24=12$

$4 \times 8 = 32 \div 2 = 16 - 2 = 14$

cm²

Find the word that means the same, or nearly the same, as the word on the left.

Example: **wide**   flat   straight   <u>broad</u>   long

9. **flourish**   complete   gain   glorify   ~~burgeon~~   *to grow rapidly, opposite of shrink*

10. **sustenance**   vigour   nourishment   ingestion   supplement

11. **detached**   aloof   prejudiced   ignorant   oblivious

12. **target**   quarry   total   harassment   allocation   *~~things~~ victim, target*

13. **subsequently**   subjectively   afterwards   erstwhile   ensuing

14. **ransack**   <u>pillage</u>   explore   accuse   rummage   *steal, cause distraction*

Complete the word on the right so that it means the opposite, or nearly the opposite, of the word on the left.

Example: heavy   l i g h t

15. agitated   s _ r _ _ e

16. affluence   _ o _ e r _ y

17. replenished   e _ _ a _ s t _ d

18. heedfully   _ a _ e _ e _ s l y

19. organised   h _ p _ a z _ r d

/ 19

36

Q1-10 will test your **verbal reasoning** skills.
You have **4 minutes** to complete Q1-10.

Choose the correct words to complete the passage below.

It is incredible to think that over 65 million years ago, dinosaurs

1. ☐ stalk
   ☐ maundered
   ☐ roamed   Earth.
   ☐ pursued

Today, paleontologists (scientists who

2. ☐ explore
   ☐ critique   dinosaurs), have a wealth of
   ☐ study
   ☐ scrutiny

3. ☐ displaying
   ☐ buried
   ☐ interred   fossils at their disposal to assist them in learning more about these
   ☐ excavated

magnificent ancient reptiles. A

everlasting

4. ☐ immediate
   ☐ perennial
   ☐ sobering   favourite amongst many dinosaur
   ☐ especial

5. ☐ operators
   ☐ participants
   ☐ detractors   is the Triceratops, with its
   ☐ enthusiasts

6. ☐ iconic
   ☐ uniquely
   ☐ draconic   horns and a large
   ☐ rarity

protective shield on its head. This dinosaur has been frequently portrayed

flag Part of discribe displayed painting drolled

7. ☐ to
   ☐ in
   ☐ on
   ☐ onto

films and television programmes, making it an immediately recognisable remnant of

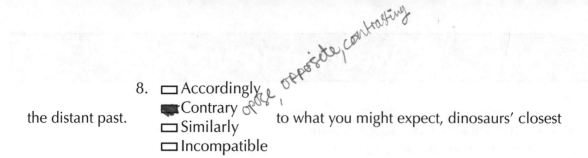

8.   ☐ Accordingly   *opose, opposite, contrasting*
     ■ Contrary   to what you might expect, dinosaurs' closest
     ☐ Similarly
     ☐ Incompatible

the distant past.

living relatives on the planet today are birds. In fact, chickens are thought to be

9.   ☐ progeniture   10. ☐ frenetic
     ☐ linked   ☐ menace
     ■ descendants   of the   ☐ terrorise   Tyrannosaurus Rex — information worth
     ☐ relative   ■ formidable

alarming fierce intimidating

bearing in mind the next time you are about to call someone 'chicken'!

> Q11-21 will test your **non-verbal reasoning** skills.
> You have **6 minutes** to complete Q11-21.

Find the figure in each row that is most unlike the others.

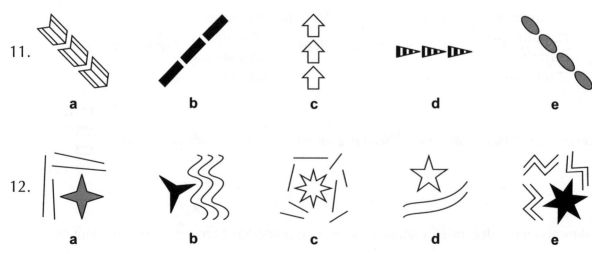

11.   a   b   c   d   e

12.   a   b   c   d   e

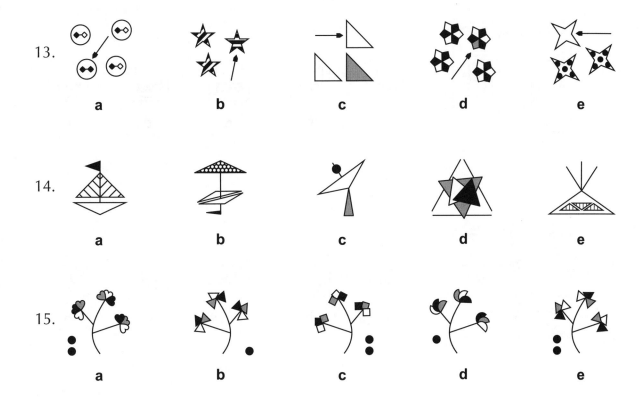

13.
    a   b   c   d   e

14.
    a   b   c   d   e

15.
    a   b   c   d   e

Work out which of the options best fits in place of the missing square in the grid.

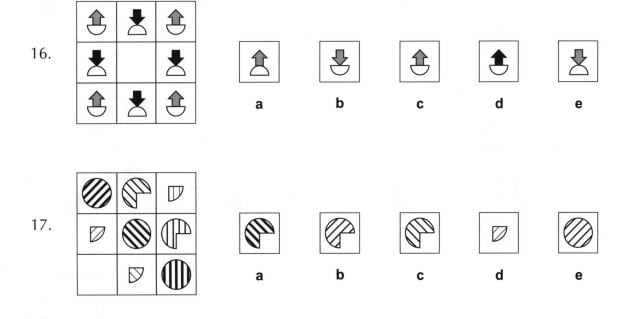

16.
    a   b   c   d   e

17.
    a   b   c   d   e

39

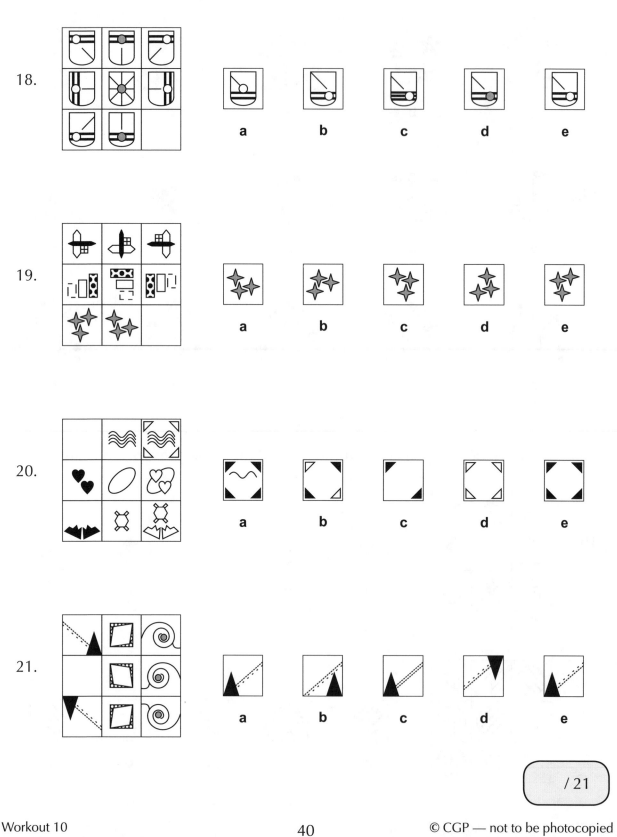

18.

a   b   c   d   e

19.

a   b   c   d   e

20.

a   b   c   d   e

21.

a   b   c   d   e

/ 21

40

These puzzles are a fun way to practise **spotting changes** and **word-making**.

Clothing Catastrophe

Colin has ruined two of his favourite T-shirts in the wash. Look at how the first T-shirt has changed, then match the second T-shirt to its ruined design.

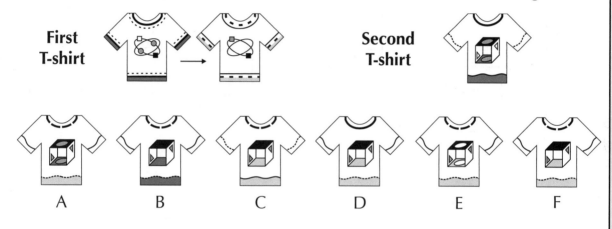

First T-shirt

Second T-shirt

A   B   C   D   E   F

Word Storm

Help Marvin to find a path of words about **weather** in the group of letters on the right. You can move one step at a time in any direction. Each step can only be used once. Draw a line showing the correct path and fill in the words on the lines below.

S T O __ __

__ __ __ __ __

__ __ __ __ __ __ __

__ __ __ __ __ __ __ __ __

__ __ __ __ __ __

Q1-7 will test your **non-verbal reasoning** skills.
You have **4 minutes** to complete Q1-7.

Work out which option is a top-down 2D view of the 3D figure on the left.

1.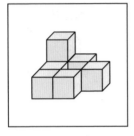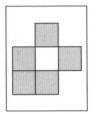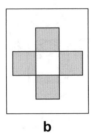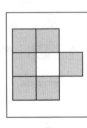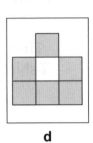

   a **b** **c** **d**

2.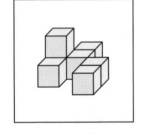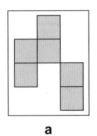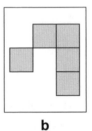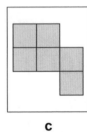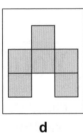

   a **b** **c** **d**

3.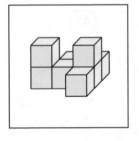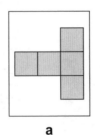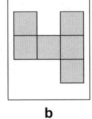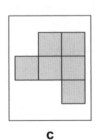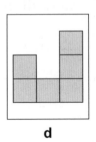

   a **b** **c** **d**

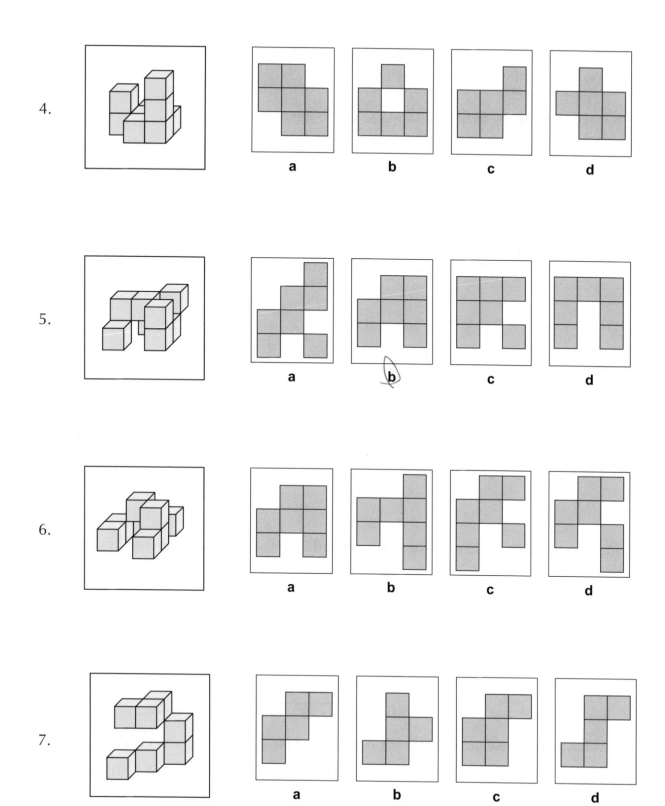

4.   **a**   **b**   **c**   **d**

5.   **a**   **b**   **c**   **d**

6.   **a**   **b**   **c**   **d**

7.   **a**   **b**   **c**   **d**

43

> Q8-15 will test your **maths** skills.
> You have **6 minutes** to complete Q8-15.

8. Use estimating to find 1218×52. Circle the correct option.

    A   1260   **C**   168 398   **E**   24 556

    B   43 116   **D**   63 336

9. The ratio of knives to forks in Sylvia's kitchen drawer is $3:2$. There are 21 knives in the drawer. How many forks are in the drawer?

10. Norah is saving up to buy a table. So far she has saved £33.50, which is $\frac{1}{6}$ of the price of the table. What is the price of the table?

11. On the coordinate grid, the line is moved 2 units to the right and 3 units down.

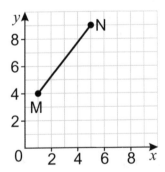

What are the new coordinates of points M and N? Circle the correct option.

    A   M(2, 8), N(6, 9)   **C**   M(6, 8), N(7, 6)   **E**   M(1, 3), N(6, 7)

    B   M(3, 1), N(7, 6)   **D**   M(3, 1), N(5, 7)

12.   What is $215.8 \times 3.6 + 6.4 \times 215.8$?

13.   Harvey earns money by mowing lawns. He charges 50 pence per m² of lawn that he mows. How much will he earn for mowing the lawn shown below?

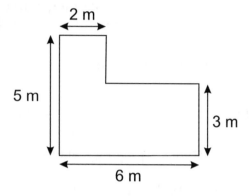

£

14.   Dustin's book has 70 pages. He has read 65% of the pages.
       How many pages has he read?

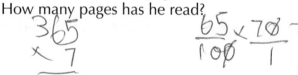

$$\frac{65}{100} \times \frac{70}{1} = \frac{455}{10} = 45.5$$

$$\begin{array}{r} 3\cancel{6}5 \\ \times\ 7 \\ \hline 455 \end{array}$$

45.50

15.   The first four terms of a sequence are shown below.

$$3 + 2a,\quad 6 + 4a,\quad 9 + 6a,\quad 12 + 8a$$

If $a = 2$, what is the sixth number in the sequence?
Circle the correct option.

A 26	**C** 36	**E** 42
B 35	**D** 40	

/ 15

Workout 11

Q1-17 will test your **verbal reasoning** skills.
You have **6 minutes** to complete Q1-17.

In each question below, the words can be rearranged to form a sentence.
One word doesn't fit in the sentence. Underline the word that doesn't fit.

Example: red   the   has   <u>ride</u>   girl   bicycle   a

1.   travel   flying   world   over   all   want   the   really   to   I

2.   happy   with   my   me   smiles   playing   school   friends   makes

3.   made   I   cupcakes   save   party   ate   the   nobody   those   that   for

4.   invisible   make   to   camouflage   vanished   soldiers   the   helped   their

5.   excel   ballerina   her   could   not   the   perform   routine   dance

Three of the words in each list are linked. Mark the word that is not related to these three.

Example: journal   diary   <u>textbook</u>   notebook

6.   knoll   bank   mound   ravine

7.   wire   cable   knot   lead

8.   scatter   pepper   sprinkle   dip

9.   secure   anchor   snatch   bind

10.   crime   witness   officer   suspect

11.   welder   plumber   electrician   apprentice

Complete the word on the right so that it means the opposite, or nearly the opposite, of the word on the left.

Example: heavy [l][i][g][h][t]

12. ameliorate [ ][o][r][s][ ][ ]

13. love [ ][b][ ][ ][r]

14. sluggish [ ][n][e][ ][g][ ][t][ ][c]

15. scarcity [a][ ][u][n][ ][a][ ][ ][e]

16. delicate [d][ ][r][ ][b][ ][e]

17. sceptic [b][ ][l][ ][ ][ ][e][r]

Q18-24 will test your **non-verbal reasoning** skills. You have **4 minutes** to complete Q18-24.

Work out which option would look like the figure on the left if it was reflected over the line.

18.

Reflect

a   b   c   d

19.

Reflect

a   b   c   d

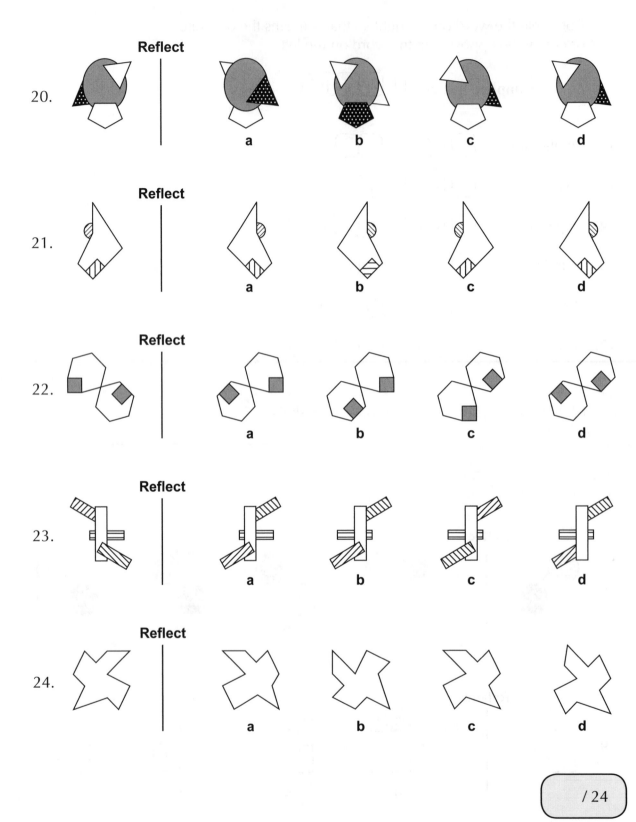

Reflect

20.

a b c d

Reflect

21.

a b c d

Reflect

22.

a b c d

Reflect

23.

a b c d

Reflect

24.

a b c d

/ 24

48

Workout 13

Q1-7 will test your **maths** skills.
You have **6 minutes** to complete Q1-7.

1. Which of the following is not equivalent to 12? Circle the correct option.

   A 6 + 6   **C** 23 – 11   **E** –4 + 16

   B 5 + 7   **D** 33 – 22

2. Sebastian has £23.73 in his wallet. On his way to lunch he finds £5 on the floor and keeps it. He spends £7.28 on his lunch. How much money is left in Sebastian's wallet?

   £ [ ][ ] . [ ][ ]

Jade is out running. The distance she has run is shown in the graph below.

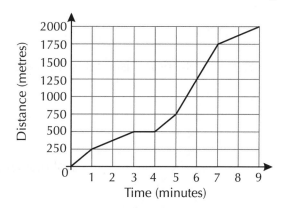

3. How far has Jade run in the last 4 minutes?

   [ ][ ][ ][ ] m

4. If Jade continues to run 2000 m every 9 minutes, how long would it take her to run 10 km?

   [ ][ ][ ] minutes

49

5. The table shows the amount of water five people drank in a day.
    Use the approximation 1 pint ≈ 0.6 litres.

Ricardo	Ernest	Kat	Justin	Marshall
2.5 pints	3.7 pints	1.8 litres	2.4 litres	1 pint

Who drank the most water? Circle the correct option.

A Ricardo   **C** Kat   **E** Marshall

B Ernest   **D** Justin

6. What is $1/2 \div 1/8$?

7. The diagram below shows a right-angled isosceles triangle.

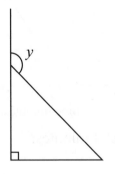

not drawn accurately

What is the size of angle y?

Q8-19 will test your **verbal reasoning** skills.
You have **4 minutes** to complete Q8-19.

Mark the word outside the brackets that has a similar meaning to the words in both sets of brackets.

Example: (twig   branch)   (fasten   attach)   glue <u>stick</u> affix bough

8.   (video   tape)   (chart   document)   shoot   archive   record   retain

9.   (circle   disc)   (stage   heat)   oval   spiral   phase   round

10.   (weave   wind)   (fibre   strand)   spin   thread   wire   braid

11.   (serious   important)   (unsmiling   sombre)   grave   muted   fatal   adverse

12.   (fee   tariff)   (count   tally)   index   account   tax   toll

13.   (waver   dither)   (stammer   stumble)   quiver   cower   falter   recoil

Find the word that means the same, or nearly the same, as the word on the left.

Example: **wide**   flat   straight   <u>broad</u>   long

14. **deafening**   boisterous   shrill   tumultuous   reverberating

15. **resolve**   extract   scheme   interpret   determine

16. **lustrous**   radiant   alluring   graceful   exquisite

17. **demolish**   depose   raze   deplete   collapse

18. **wicked**   morbid   grim   unbearable   heinous

19. **turmoil**   skirmish   setback   unrest   struggle

/ 19

51   Workout 13

Have a go at these puzzles for some fun with **spotting connections** and **3D shapes**.

A Sneaky Spider

Dress code

Webby Eight-Legs is trying to sneak into a celebrity spider party. There's a strict dress code, so Webby needs to make sure that she wears the correct outfit.

Which of Webby's outfits is most like the dress code?

A 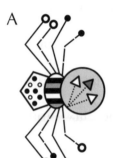   B 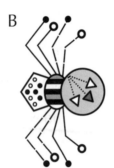   C 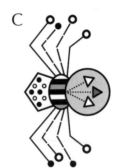   D

Cube Conundrum

Andrew builds a cube using identical smaller cubes. The cube he makes is 4 small cubes tall. Andrew then decides to paint a cross on each face of the new cube, as shown below. How many of the smaller cubes have 3 whole faces painted? How many cubes have an area equivalent to one face painted? How many cubes have no paint on them at all?

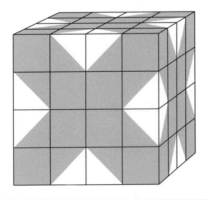

Q1-11 will test your **non-verbal reasoning** skills.
You have **6 minutes** to complete Q1-11.

Work out which of the four cubes can be made from the net.

1.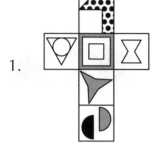

    a   **b**   **c**   **d**

2.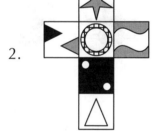

    a   **b**   **c**   **d**

3.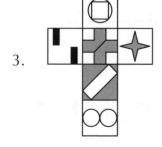

    a   **b**   **c**   **d**

       53

Look at how the first bug changes to become the second bug. Then work out which option would look like the third bug if you changed it in the same way.

4.

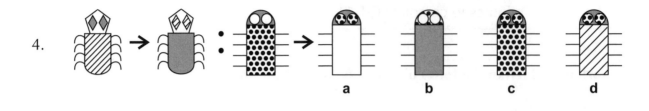

                                 a   **b**   **c**   **d**

5.

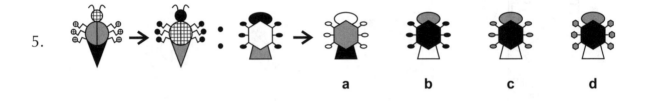

                                 a   **b**   **c**   **d**

6.

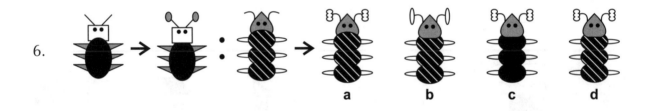

                                 a   **b**   **c**   **d**

Work out which of the options best fits in place of the missing square in the series.

7.

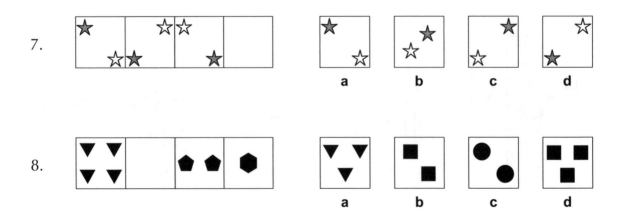

8.

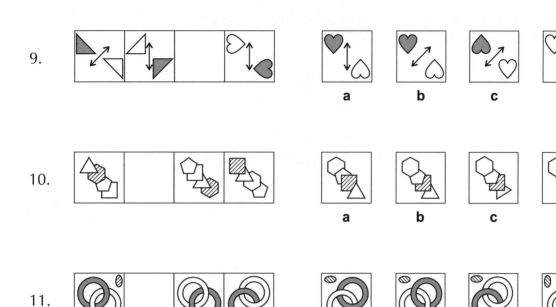

9.

10.

11.

Q12-16 will test your **maths** skills.
You have **4 minutes** to complete Q12-16.

12. In which of the following does 7 have the lowest value? Circle the correct option.

   A   43 781
   B   239 973
   C   9789
   D   57 000
   E   971 063

13. Tessa runs 21 miles in 3 hours. On average how many miles did she run per hour?

   ☐☐ miles

55

14. If the pentagon below was cut along all its lines of symmetry, how many pieces would there be?

15. There are 300 steps leading to a temple. Each step is the same height and the height of 8 steps is 200 cm. Work out the total height of the steps.

 m

16. Pierre and Carlo both go running. Pierre ran 20 km. Carlo ran 60% further than Pierre. How far did Carlo run?
    Use the approximation 8 km ≈ 5 miles. Circle the correct option.

A 7.5 miles	**C** 20 miles	**E** 32 miles
B 12.5 miles	**D** 30 km	

/ 16

Q1-7 will test your **comprehension** skills.
You have **6 minutes** to complete Q1-7.

Read this passage carefully and answer the questions that follow.

An abridged extract from 'In November'

With loitering step and quiet eye,
Beneath the low November sky,
I wandered in the woods, and found
A clearing, where the broken ground
5 Was scattered with black stumps and briers,
And the old wreck of forest fires.
It was a bleak and sandy spot,
And, all about, the vacant plot
Was peopled and inhabited
10 By scores* of mulleins** long since dead.
Not plants at all they seemed to me,
But rather some spare company
Of hermit folk, who long ago,
Wandering in bodies to and fro,
15 Had chanced upon this lonely way,
And rested thus, till death one day
Surprised them at their compline*** prayer,
And left them standing lifeless there.

There was no sound about the wood
20 Save the wind's secret stir. I stood
Among the mullein-stalks as still
As if myself had grown to be
One of their sombre company,
A body without wish or will
25 And as I stood, quite suddenly,
Down from a furrow in the sky
The sun shone out a little space
Across that silent sober place,
Over the sand heaps and brown sod,
30 The mulleins and dead goldenrod****,
And passed beyond the thickets grey,
And lit the fallen leaves that lay,
Level and deep within the wood,
A rustling yellow multitude.

Archibald Lampman

* scores — *a large number*

** mulleins — *flowering plants*

*** compline — *a Christian service that takes place in the evening*

**** goldenrod — *a plant with yellow flowers*

Answer these questions about the text that you've just read.
Circle the letter that matches the correct answer.

1. The narrator is walking "With loitering step" (line 1). What does this mean?

   A   The narrator often walks in the woods.

   B   The narrator intends to make trouble.

   C   The narrator is in pain.

   D   The narrator is walking slowly.

2. Which of the following statements best describes the clearing in lines 4-10?

   A   It is completely empty.

   B   It has been damaged by animals.

   C   It has been destroyed by fire.

   D   It used to be inhabited by people.

3. What does the word "bleak" (line 7) mean?

   A   Vivid   C   Disastrous

   B   Uneasy   D   Desolate

4. Which of the following statements about the narrator is true?

   A   He compares the plants in the clearing to people.

   B   He says a prayer in the clearing.

   C   He worries that someone is watching him.

   D   He meets some travellers in the woods.

5. Line 15 says "Had chanced upon this lonely way". What does this mean?

   A   Had hoped to cure loneliness

   B   Had accidentally found a secluded path

   C   Had felt very lucky

   D   Had enjoyed the solitude of the place

6. Which of the following is not mentioned in lines 19-34?

   A   The sound of the wind

   B   Dead plants

   C   A ray of sunlight

   D   Birds singing

7. What does "rustling yellow multitude" (line 34) refer to?

   A   The sun illuminating the woods

   B   Flowers in the undergrowth

   C   Leaves on the ground

   D   The sounds of woodland creatures

Q8-14 will test your **non-verbal reasoning** skills.
You have **4 minutes** to complete Q8-14.

Work out which option is most like the two figures on the left.

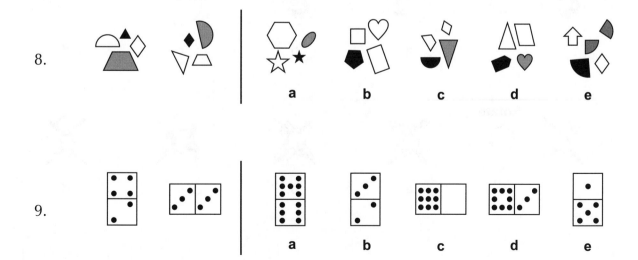

8.

     a   b   c   d   e

9.

     a   b   c   d   e

59   Workout 15

10.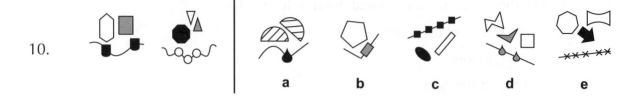

              a   **b**   **c**   **d**   **e**

Work out which option would look like the figure on the left if it was rotated.

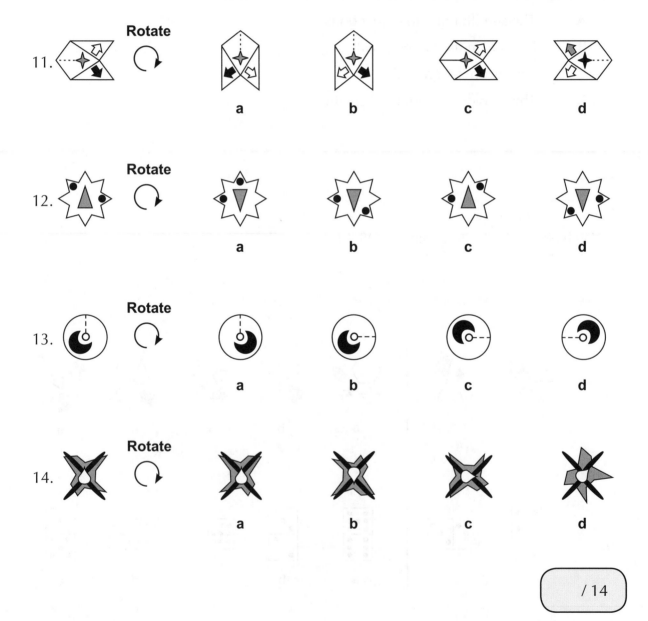

/ 14

Q1-5 will test your **maths** skills.
You have **4 minutes** to complete Q1-5.

1. What is 24 ÷ 6? Give your answer in Roman numerals.

2. What is the volume of the cuboid shown below?

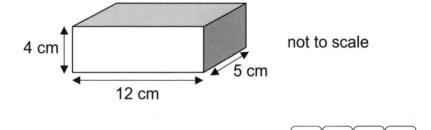

not to scale

☐☐☐☐ cm³

3. Amelia had a summer job in August last year. She earned £41 a day and worked a total of 23 days. How much did she earn in total?

    A £892   **C** £963   **E** £1029
    B £943   **D** £977

4. If $x = 3$, which of the following numbers is equal to $x^2 + 3x$?
Circle the correct option.

    A 6   **C** 12   **E** 18
    B 9   **D** 15

5. There are four difficulty levels of ski runs on a mountain and each level is represented by a colour. The pie chart shows the number of people that skied each colour of run in an hour, out of a total of 320. How many people skied on blue runs?

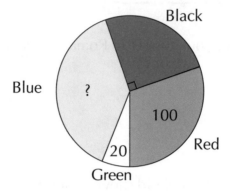

Q6-24 will test your **verbal reasoning** skills.
You have **6 minutes** to complete Q6-24.

Three of the words in each list are linked. Mark the word that is not related to these three.

Example: journal   diary   <u>textbook</u>   notebook

6. tundra   grassland   desert   territory

7. trot   canter   linger   gallop

8. zealous   empowered   passionate   avid

9. interval   epoch   age   era

10. adjacent   opposite   longer   above

Find the word that means the opposite, or nearly the opposite, of the word on the left.

Example: **first** later <u>last</u> next beginning

11. **famished**   copious   ravenous   sated   mitigated

12. **idle**   influential   frivolous   driven   industrious

13. **civilised**   unkind   fierce   inhumane   barbaric

14. **untangle**   engage   entwine   extricate   encircle

15. **falsehood**   principle   fallacy   precision   verity

16. **honour**   fidelity   disgrace   renown   blemish

17. **disperse**   convene   enclose   mobilise   diffuse

Complete the word on the right so that it means the same, or nearly the same, as the word on the left.

Example: scared a f r a i d

18. hypnotise   m _ s _ _ r _ s e

19. outline   s _ l h _ u _ t _ e

20. dubious   d _ u _ _ _ u l

21. unimportant   n _ g _ i g _ b l e

22. negotiate   _ _ g _ _ l e

23. spirited   a _ i m _ _ e d

24. profusion   _ u _ t i _ u _ e

/ 24

Workout 16

These puzzles are a great way to practise your **word-making** and **algebra** skills.

Wobbly Words

Fill in the missing words in the rickety rope bridges. Each word is one letter different from the previous word. Some words have been filled in for you.

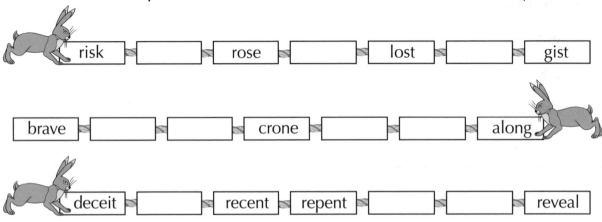

| risk | | rose | | lost | | gist |

| brave | | | crone | | | along |

| deceit | | recent | repent | | | reveal |

Combination Calculation

Esteban is always forgetting the combination to his safe, so he wrote some clues to help himself remember:

- The first number is the smallest prime number multiplied by the second smallest prime number.

- The second number is the number of degrees in a right angle divided by 30.

- If the second number is x then the third number is $\frac{x}{5} + \frac{14}{10}$.

- If the third number is y then the fourth number is $4y - (3 + y)$.

What is Esteban's combination?

Workout 17

Q1-10 will test your **verbal reasoning** skills.
You have **4 minutes** to complete Q1-10.

Fill in the missing letters to complete the words in the following passage.

Since the Ancient Greek philosopher Plato wrote about the city of Atlantis over

1.   2000 years ago, it has [c][a][ ][t][i][ ][ ][t][e][d] people around the world.

2.   Atlantis was said to have been a mighty and [ ][r][ ][s][p][ ][ ][o][u][s]

3.   civilisation, but its [r][ ][s][ ][d][ ][ ][t][s] were believed to have greatly

4.   angered their gods with increasingly [i][ ][m][ ][ ][a][l] behaviour. As a

5.   punishment, the gods [ ][u][ ][m][e][ ][ ][e][d] Atlantis beneath the sea.

Many people have searched for the lost city and its treasures, but with no

6.   success. Very [ ][i][ ][t][ ][e] trustworthy evidence about the location

7.   of Atlantis exists, although several [ ][n][ ][r][ ][v][ ][n] theories have been

proposed by historians and Atlantis enthusiasts alike. It is now thought that if

8.   Atlantis did exist, a volcanic [e][ ][u][ ][ ][i][o][ ] is more likely to have

9.   been responsible for its [c][a][ ][a][s][t][ ][o][ ][ ][i][c] end than any

kind of divine intervention. Although most agree that Atlantis was nothing more

10. than a myth, [ ][p][ ][c][ ][l][a][ ][i][o][n] remains rife about exactly

where this legendary city might lie hidden beneath the waves.

65

Players in a quiz gain 2 points for answering a question correctly and lose 1 point for answering one incorrectly. The scores of five players halfway through the quiz are shown below.

Derek	Iris	Orla	Anderson	Martha
0	2	−3	11	−6

11. If Orla gets four questions wrong in a row, what will her score be?
Circle the correct option.

   A 1   **C** −1   **E** −11
   B −4   **D** −7

12. In the second half, Iris doesn't play and Martha gets every question correct. After how many questions did Martha catch up with Iris's score?

13. The diagram below shows a net for a square-based pyramid, where the triangular faces are equilateral. What is the perimeter of the net?

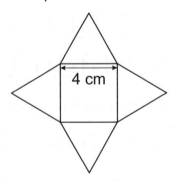

4 cm

___ cm

14. $5698 \div 56 = 101.75$. What is $5698 \div 5600$?

15. A ferry journey is 6 hours and 40 minutes long. Theo has been on the ferry for 5 hours. What percentage of the journey has he already completed? Circle the correct option.

A	90%	**C**	85%	**E**	75%
B	70%	**D**	60%		

16. The prices of two holidays are shown in the table below.

Holiday	Flights	Per Day
Spain	£230	£50
Greece	£320	£30

What is the difference in the total price between the two holidays for seven days? Circle the correct option.

A	£90	**C**	£10	**E**	£70
B	£50	**D**	£30		

17. The diagram shows a rectangular picture frame. The shaded border of the frame is made from 5 cm wide pieces of wood. What is the area of the shaded border of the frame?

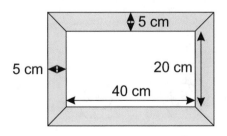

not to scale

☐☐☐ cm²

/ 17

Workout 18

Work out which of the options best fits in place of the missing hexagon in the grid.

1.

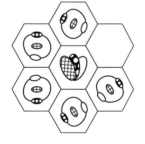

     a   b   c   d

2.

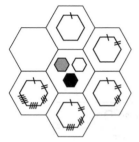

     a   b   c   d

3.

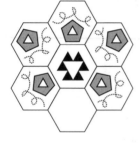

     a   b   c   d

4.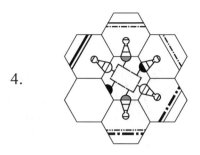

a	**b**	**c**	**d**

Work out which of the four cubes can be made from the net.

5.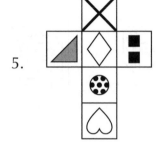

a	**b**	**c**	**d**

6.

a	**b**	**c**	**d**

7.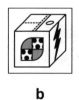

a	**b**	**c**	**d**

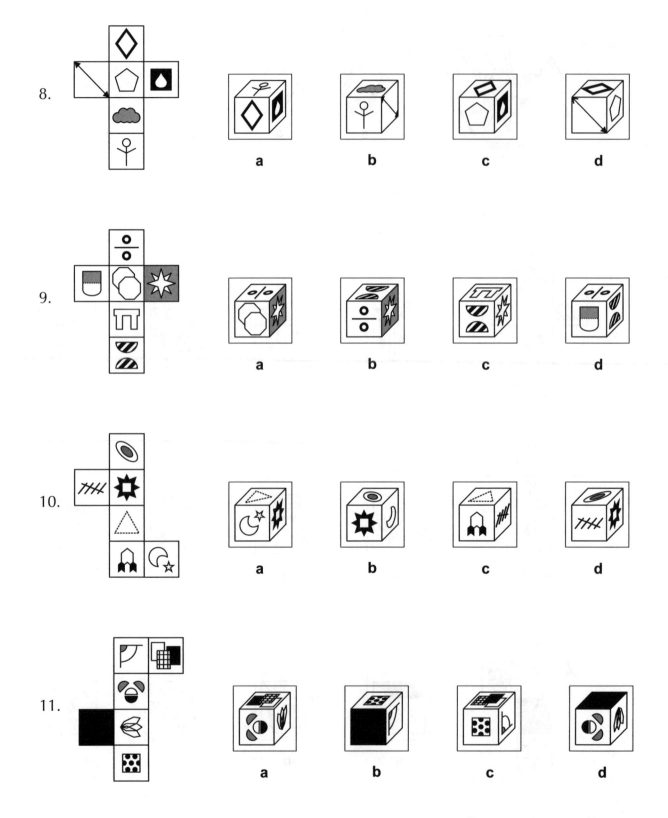

8.

a b c d

9.

a b c d

10.

a b c d

11.

a b c d

In each question below, the words can be rearranged to form a sentence.
One word doesn't fit in the sentence. Underline the word that doesn't fit.

Example: red   the   has   <u>ride</u>   girl   bicycle   a

12. planes   loved   the   people   teaching   pilot   fly   to   learnt   how

13. thousand   over   growth   live   can   trees   one   oak   for   years

14. lots   cheek   saved   hamsters   store   pouches   their   in   food   can   of

15. Queen   swans   English   crown   Her   to   belong   the   Majesty   many

16. way   anyone   this   was   could   there   prepared   must   have   for   no

17. burglar   a   police   testimony   crime   Mark's   the   helped   catch   to

Mark the word outside the brackets that has a similar meaning to the words in both sets of brackets.

Example: (twig   branch)   (fasten   attach)   glue   <u>stick</u>   affix   bough

18. (tedious   tiresome)   (dreary   colourless)   stale   plain   passive   dull

19. (tremble   vibrate)   (unnerve   scare)   shake   bother   faze   distress

20. (swelling   pimple)   (churn   seethe)   steam   flare   ulcer   boil

21. (carry   convey)   (support   brace)   tote   endure   bear   reinforce

22. (valley   depression)   (vessel   bowl)   basin   gully   tank   ditch

23. (screen   mask)   (cape   robe)   cover   shawl   cloak   facade

/ 23

Q1-7 will test your **non-verbal reasoning** skills.
You have **4 minutes** to complete Q1-7.

Work out which set of blocks can be put together to make the 3D figure on the left.

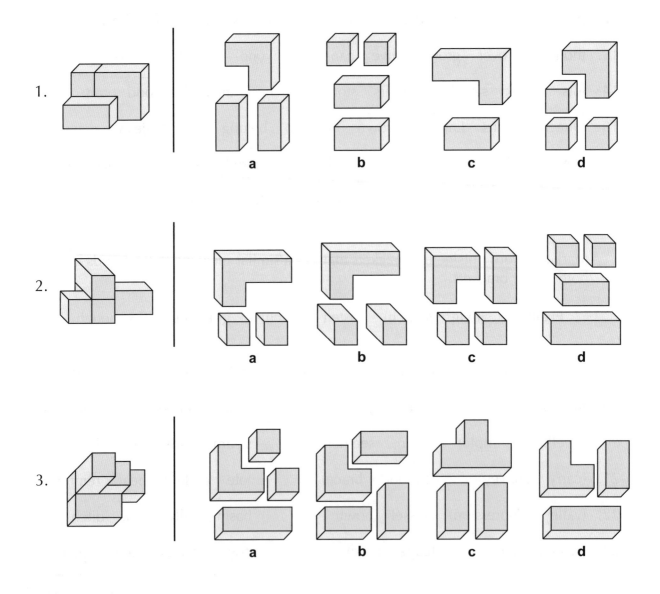

1.

a   b   c   d

2.

a   b   c   d

3.

a   b   c   d

Work out which 3D figure in the grey box has been rotated to make the new 3D figure.

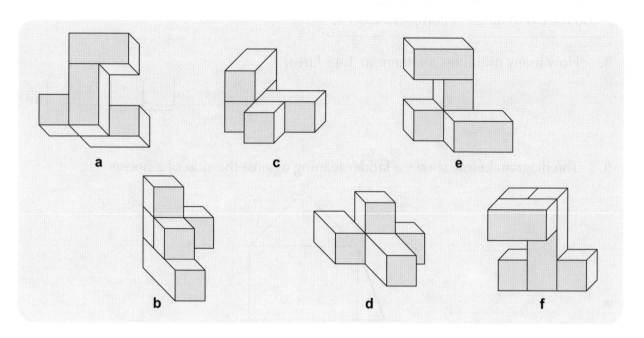

a

c

e

b

d

f

4.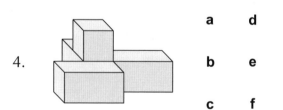

a   d

b   e

c   f

5.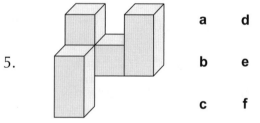

a   d

b   e

c   f

6.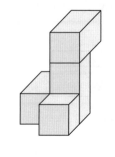

a   d

b   e

c   f

7.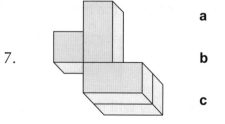

a   d

b   e

c   f

Workout 19

8.   How many millilitres are there in 3.45 litres?

9.   The diagram below shows a ladder leaning against the side of a house.

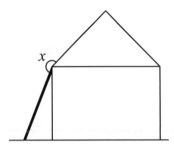

   Which of the following is the most likely size of angle x? Circle the correct option.

   A   203°   **C**   175°   **E**   86°

   B   250°   **D**   157°

10. What is 36% of 800?

11. A tree sheds exactly half its leaves every day. The table below shows the number
     of leaves left on the tree at the end of the first 3 days.

Day	1	2	3
Leaves	96	48	24

   On what day will the tree have an odd number of leaves left?

   Day

12. Jonathan is sorting out his recycling. He has 15 plastic items, 8 tins and 4 glass items. What proportion of Jonathan's recycling items are plastic? Circle the correct option.

A $^2/_5$ **C** $^{13}/_{27}$ **E** $^5/_9$

B $^1/_2$ **D** $^2/_3$

13. Hassan lives 8 miles from school. If Hassan travels 12 miles per hour on his bike how long will it take him to cycle to school? Circle the correct option.

A   20 minutes

B   45 minutes

C   30 minutes

D   15 minutes

E   40 minutes

14. The diagram below shows a fan. The fan has a diameter of $4a$ cm. The fan blades are equilateral triangles.

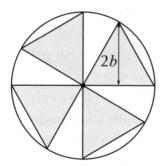

Which of the following expressions describes the area of the shaded fan blades? Circle the correct option.

A $16ab$ **C** $8ab$ **E** $6a^2$

B $^1/_2 a + 4b$ **D** $4a + 2b$

/ 14

Workout 19

Q1-7 will test your **comprehension** skills.
You have **6 minutes** to complete Q1-7.

Read this passage carefully and answer the questions that follow.

The Old Well

The hundred-year-old well was an incongruous piece of history on the edge of a housing estate that had existed for less than a decade. Stones were missing from the once-neat circle, and there was a thick coating of moss around its rim. When you peered over the edge, you couldn't see the bottom — there was only a deep, fierce

5   darkness that seemed to go on forever.

Alice's brother Chris — who always thought he knew best — claimed that it was a portal to another world. He said aliens and monsters crawled out of it at night and skulked back down at sunrise. Alice had made it her mission to find out for herself, even though Chris had scoffed that the monsters were far too clever to be caught.

10   She shone her torch down into the well's unfathomable depths. The council had installed a spindly grate over the top after local residents complained it was a hazard. Monsters probably weren't fazed by the council's health and safety measures though. Through the grate, Alice's torch illuminated the sludge and grime of the discoloured stone walls, but not much else. She knew she would never get a sighting of a monster

15   in the daytime, but perhaps remnants of a visit would survive — a scale or a feather, or maybe even a footprint if she was lucky.

Alice's hand slipped and she dropped the torch. It lurched through the holes in the grate and tumbled down the well with a resounding clatter, banging against the stone walls. Alice's heart was pounding. She took a step back. A low, thunderous rumble

20   was rising from deep within the well.

Answer these questions about the text that you've just read.
Circle the letter that matches the correct answer.

1. Which of the following statements must be false?

    A   It is difficult to see inside the well.

    B   There is vegetation growing on the well.

    C   The housing estate was built before the well.

    D   The well is located near an urban area.

2. Which of the following words best describes the condition of the well?

    A   Intact   **C**   Imposing

    B   Dilapidated   **D**   Resplendent

3. How does Chris feel about Alice's attempt to investigate the well?

    A   He is supportive of her efforts.

    B   He is sceptical about her plan.

    C   He is worried for her safety.

    D   He wants to find the monsters first.

4. Why is there a grate on top of the well?

    A   To prevent monsters climbing out.

    B   To stop people investigating the well.

    C   To prevent accidents.

    D   To preserve the well.

5. According to the text, what does Alice hope to prove from her investigation?

    A   That a monster has been at the well.

    B   That she isn't afraid of monsters.

    C   That monsters can have feathers or scales.

    D   That the well is a dangerous place.

6. Which of the following must be true?

 A   The torch is caught by the metal grate.

 B   Alice reaches down into the well to get her torch.

 C   The torch illuminates the bottom of the well.

 D   The torch makes a lot of noise as it falls.

7. How do you think Alice feels in line 19?

 A   Curious

 B   Ecstatic

 C   Alarmed

 D   Nonchalant

Q8-14 will test your **non-verbal reasoning** skills.
You have **4 minutes** to complete Q8-14.

Work out which option is most like the three figures on the left.

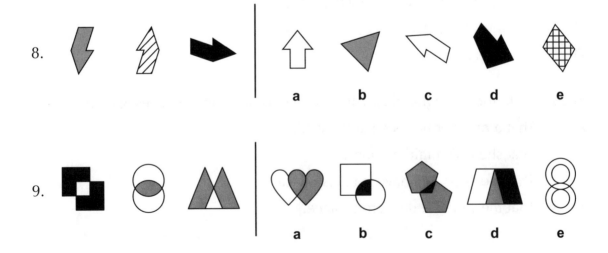

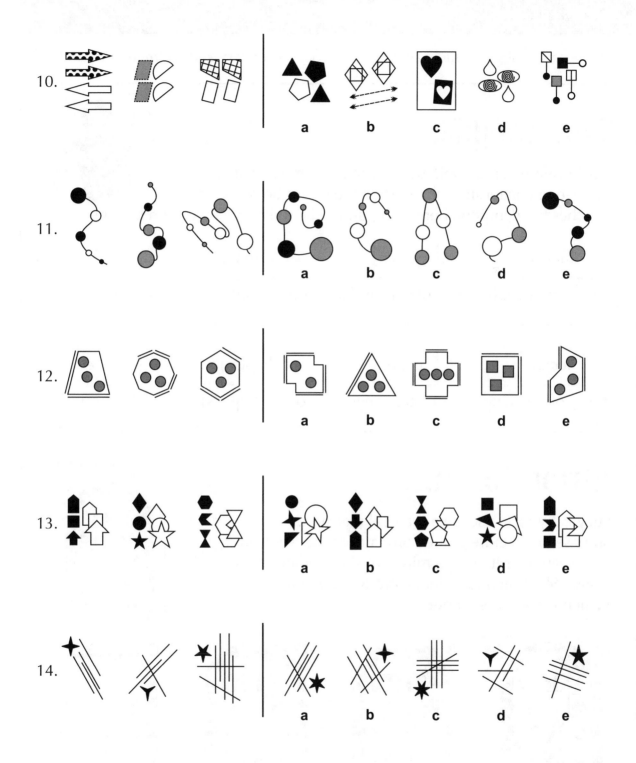

10.

    a   **b**   **c**   **d**   **e**

11.

    a   **b**   **c**   **d**   **e**

12.

    a   **b**   **c**   **d**   **e**

13.

    a   **b**   **c**   **d**   **e**

14.

    a   **b**   **c**   **d**   **e**

/ 14

Workout 20

Try these puzzles for a fun way to practise your **vocabulary** and **symmetry** skills.

Typo Trouble

Basil is typing up a book, but he's made some mistakes.
Change one letter in each word on the books below so that it
matches the definition beneath it, and write the correct word on the line.

mayor	object	torrent	health
great or crucial	completely awful	severe suffering	a fireplace
_____	_____	_____	_____

accept	grate	chapter	nature
a way of speaking	extremely angry	to speak quickly	fully grown
_____	_____	_____	_____

Mirror, Mirror...

Lucy is trying to escape a magical mansion.
She's seen a picture of the correct door, but she can
only search for it using a mirror or she'll be turned to
stone. She's seen four doors through the mirror.
Which is the correct one?

The correct door

A

B

C

D

Workout 21

Q1-7 will test your **maths** skills.
You have **6 minutes** to complete Q1-7.

1. Round 179 502 to the nearest thousand.

2. Work out the angle labelled x.

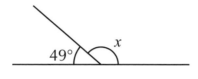

Aziz records the number of visits to his bird feeder by different types of birds. In total he records 72 visits to his bird feeder. His results are shown in the bar chart below.

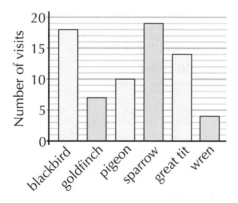

3. What is the difference between the most and fewest visits by a type of bird?

4. Aziz is putting his results into a pie chart. What will the angle of the blackbird section be? Circle the correct option.

  A 20°   **C** 120°   **E** 45°
  B 60°   **D** 90°

                                   Workout 21

5. Kile's train set off at 17:25. He arrives 8 hours and 40 minutes later. Which of the following clocks shows the time he arrived? Circle the correct option.

A 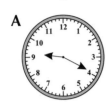 B 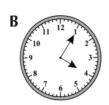 C 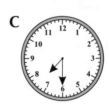 D 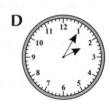 E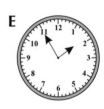

6. Nico goes fishing for two and a half hours. He catches 5 fish in the first hour, 3 fish in the second hour and 2 fish in the last half-hour. What is the mean number of fish Nico caught per hour?

7. $4a + 3b = -24$. If $b = -12$, what is the value of a? Circle the correct option.

A   24   C   5   E   3

B   12   D   4

Q8-17 will test your **verbal reasoning** skills. You have **4 minutes** to complete Q8-17.

Choose the correct words to complete the passage below.

Although pizza is now an

8.   ☐ incredible
    ☐ overwhelmingly   popular fast food, this was not
    ☐ really
    ☐ typical

always the case.

9.   ☐ Accustomed
    ☐ Traditional
    ☐ Stereotypical   pizza originates from Naples in Italy,
    ☐ Establishment

where the simple flat bread with tomato sauce provided poor families with a cheap and

10. ☐ nourishing
    ☐ enrich
    ☐ quenching   meal. Originally, there were two main types of pizza — the marinara,
    ☐ fulfilled

11. ☐ fisherman   12. ☐ supposed
    ☐ marinas   ☐ allegedly
which was eaten by   ☐ sailor   , and the margherita, which was   ☐ rumours
    ☐ seafarers   ☐ thought

named after Queen Margherita in 1889. A margherita's ingredients (tomato, mozzarella,

13. ☐ reflection
    ☐ evoke
and basil) are said to   ☐ remind   the colours of the Italian national flag.
    ☐ signified

                                                   14. ☐ across
                                                       ☐ span
After World War Two, pizza became increasingly popular   ☐ reaching   America and
                                                       ☐ cover

                                                   15. ☐ sovereign
                                                       ☐ individuals
several Italian emigrants opened their own   ☐ specialities   pizzerias. Today, rules put
                                                       ☐ independent

                                                   16. ☐ appropriate
                                                       ☐ recognised
in place to preserve Italian traditions state that an   ☐ authentic   Neapolitan pizza
                                                       ☐ legitimate

17. ☐ blend
    ☐ kneaded
must have been   ☐ working   by hand before being baked in a special wood-fired oven.
    ☐ scoured

/ 17

83

Q1-11 will test your **non-verbal reasoning** skills.
You have **6 minutes** to complete Q1-11.

Work out which option would look like the figure on the left if it was reflected over the line.

Reflect

1.

    a   **b**   **c**   **d**

Reflect

2.

    a   **b**   **c**   **d**

Reflect

3.

    a   **b**   **c**   **d**

Reflect

4.

    a   **b**   **c**   **d**

Reflect

5.

    a   **b**   **c**   **d**

Work out which option is most like the two figures on the left.

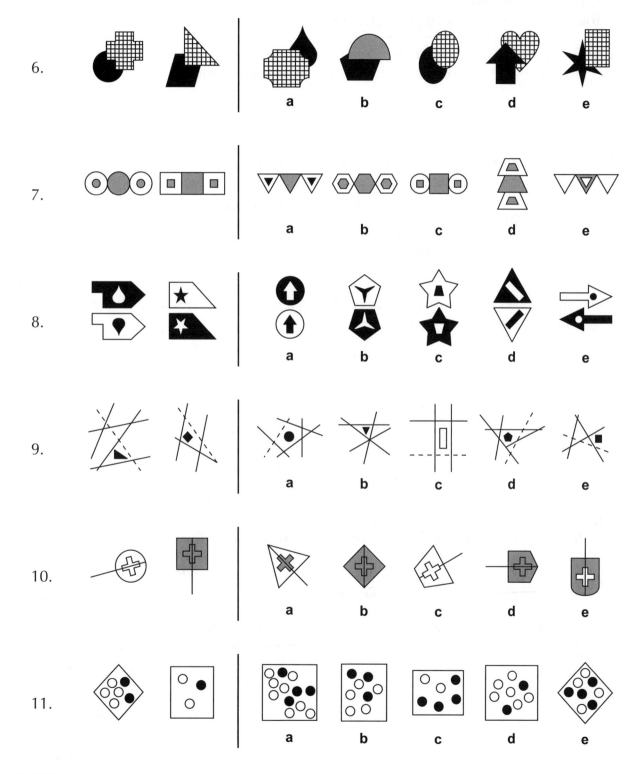

6.

7.

8.

9.

10.

11.

85

Q12-15 will test your **maths** skills.
You have **4 minutes** to complete Q12-15.

12. For every 2 pigs in a field there are 3 sheep.
    If there are 39 sheep in the field how many pigs are there?

13. What is the volume of the matchbox shown below?

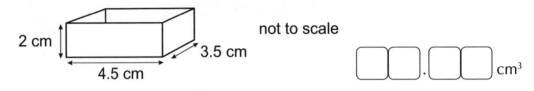

2 cm   3.5 cm   not to scale

4.5 cm

cm³

The graphs shows how the price of a salad from a restaurant increases with the number of extra items added to the salad.

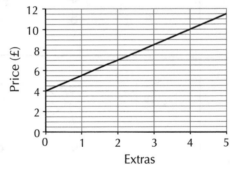

14. Gale buys one salad with 2 extras, one with 3 extras and another with
    5 extras. How much will the salads cost in total? Circle the correct option.

    A   £18   **C**   £20.50   **E**   £19
    B   £35.50   **D**   £27

15. The formula to calculate the price is $P = 4 + 1.5E$, where P is the price in pounds
    and E is the number of extras. How much would a salad with 7 extras be?

    £

/ 15

Q1-11 will test your **non-verbal reasoning** skills. You have **6 minutes** to complete Q1-11.

Look at how the first two figures are changed, and then work out which option would look like the third figure if you changed it in the same way.

1.

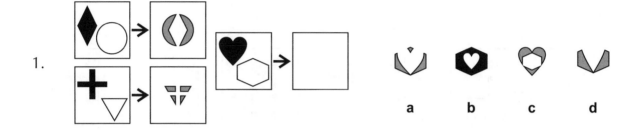

2.

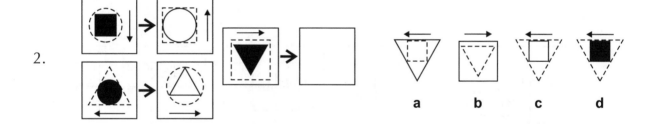

3.

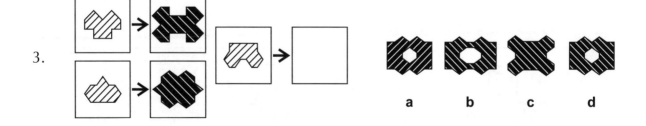

Work out which option is a top-down 2D view of the 3D figure on the left.

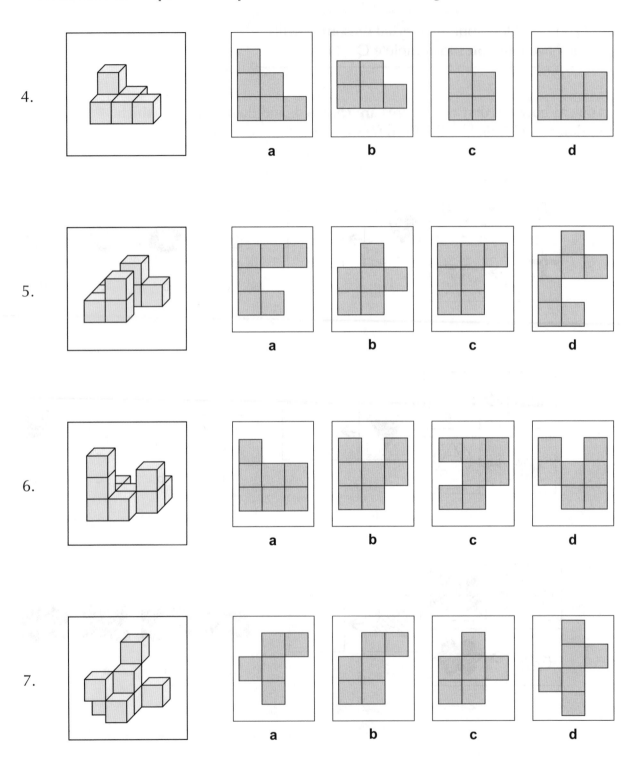

4.

a b c d

5.

a b c d

6.

a b c d

7.

a b c d

88

Work out which of the options best fits in place of the missing square in the grid.

8.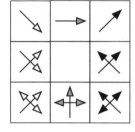

    a   b   c   d   e

9.

    a   b   c   d   e

10.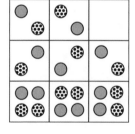

    a   b   c   d   e

11.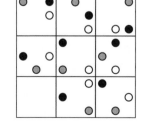

    a   b   c   d   e

Workout 23

Q12-23 will test your **verbal reasoning** skills.
You have **4 minutes** to complete Q12-23.

Find the word that means the same, or nearly the same, as the word on the left.

Example: **wide**   flat   straight   <u>broad</u>   long

12. **unfamiliar**   uncouth   atypical   foreign   displaced

13. **grumpy**   critical   cantankerous   threatening   exasperated

14. **seethe**   fume   soak   sulk   erupt

15. **vengeful**   envious   villainous   grudging   vindictive

16. **divergence**   deviation   isolation   desertion   progression

Complete the word on the right so that it means the opposite, or nearly the opposite, of the word on the left.

Example: heavy   l i g h t

17. deny   c ☐ n ☐ ☐ r m

18. extend   ☐ ☐ t ☐ a c t

19. disinterest   b ☐ ☐ s

20. blemished   ☐ l a ☐ l ☐ ☐ s

21. construct   d ☐ s ☐ ☐ s e ☐ b l e

22. distribute   c ☐ ☐ l ☐ ☐ c ☐

23. uncertainly   ☐ ☐ n f i ☐ e ☐ t l y

/ 23

Break time! These puzzles are great to practise your **angles** and **pattern-spotting** skills.

Loopy Snooker

The plan view of a parallelogram snooker table is shown on the right. When a ball hits a side, the angles it arrives and leaves at are always symmetrical — e.g:

The ball is struck and hits the top side at a 40° angle, bounces round the table and hits the top side again. Accurately draw the ball's path to find the angle it hits the top side the second time.

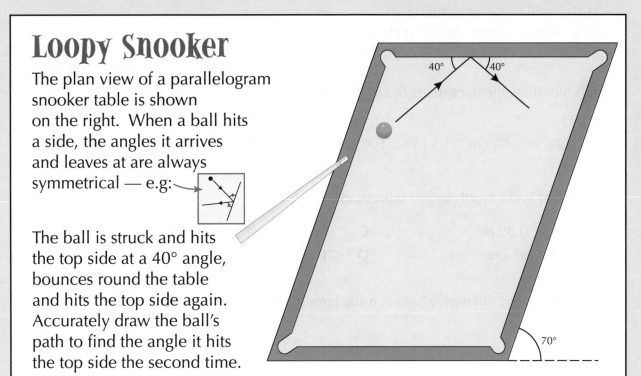

Hexagonal Havoc

Jamal made a pattern using hexagonal tiles. Hamish removed four of the tiles and mixed them up with tiles that don't fit Jamal's pattern. Find the four missing tiles.

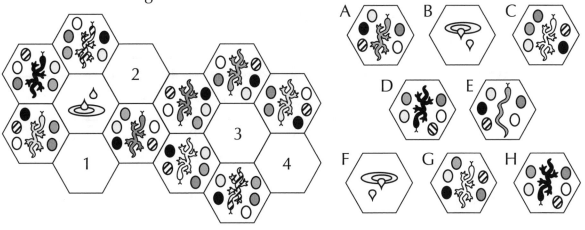

Puzzles 8

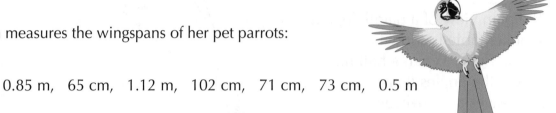

Q1-7 will test your **maths** skills.
You have **6 minutes** to complete Q1-7.

Faith measures the wingspans of her pet parrots:

0.85 m, 65 cm, 1.12 m, 102 cm, 71 cm, 73 cm, 0.5 m

1. What is the fourth largest wingspan?

   A 0.85 m   **C** 102 cm   **E** 73 cm

   B 65 cm   **D** 71 cm

2. What is the difference between the largest and smallest wingspans?

   ☐☐ cm

3. Florence is moving a shed. The grid below shows the current shaded position of the shed and the new proposed position which is shown by the dotted outline. How many units left and up does Florence need to move the shed?

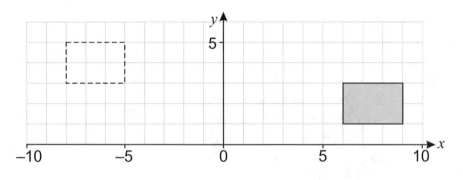

   ☐☐ left and ☐☐ up

92

4. What is 0.8 ÷ 4?

5. Bryony has 25 m² of new carpet for two rooms in her house. The sizes of the two rooms are shown below. How much carpet will Bryony have left after laying new carpet in both rooms?

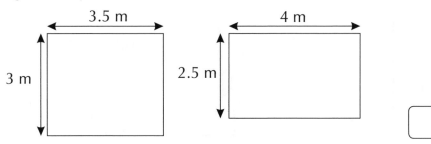

3.5 m

3 m

4 m

2.5 m

$\boxed{}\boxed{}.\boxed{}$ m²

6. Lesley has been working at a vineyard for four days. The amounts she has earned each day form a sequence and are shown below.

£33,   £36,   £39,   £42

Which of the following describes how much she earns on the nth day.?
Circle the correct option.

A	$30 + 3n$	**C**	$30n$	**E**	$3n + n$
B	$10n + 3$	**D**	$50 - 3n$		

7. Felicity cuts a $^1/_4$ off from a cube of cheese. The $^1/_4$ of the cube weighs 16 g.
If 1 cm³ of cheese weighs 1 gram, what was the height of the original cube of cheese? Circle the correct option.

A   3 cm
B   16 cm
C   8 cm
D   4 cm
E   2 cm

Work out which set of blocks can be put together to make the 3D figure on the left.

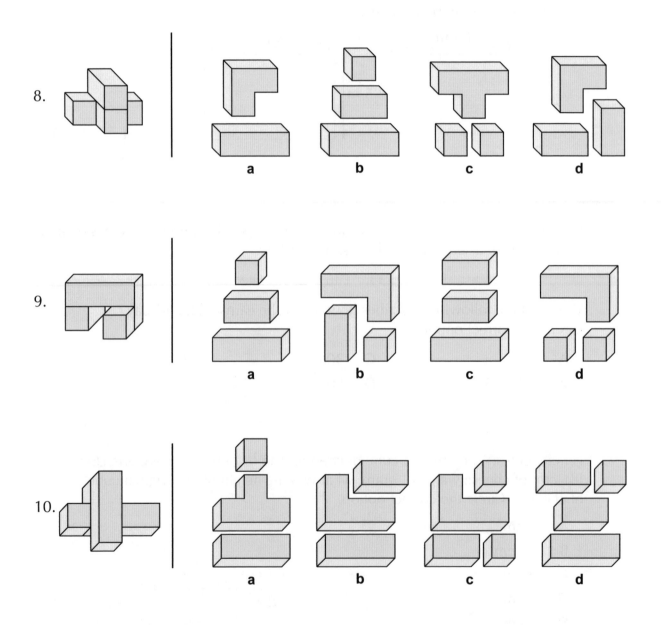

8.

  a   b   c   d

9.

  a   b   c   d

10.

  a   b   c   d

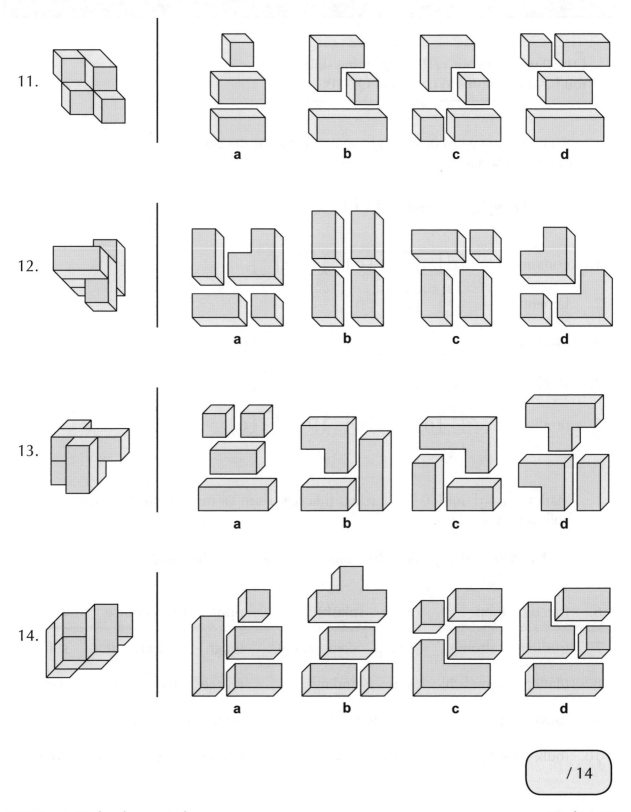

11.

12.

13.

14.

a   b   c   d

/ 14

Q1-10 will test your **verbal reasoning** skills.
You have **4 minutes** to complete Q1-10.

Complete the word on the right so that it means the same,
or nearly the same, as the word on the left.

Example: scared a f r a i d

1. committed   d _ _ i c _ t e _

2. lament   _ _ u _ n

3. disclosure   r e _ e l _ t i _ n

4. stubborn   o _ s t _ n _ t _

5. predict   _ n t _ c _ p a _ e

Mark the word outside the brackets that has a similar meaning to the words in both sets of brackets.

Example: (twig branch) (fasten attach)   glue <u>stick</u> affix bough

6. (circuit loop)   (wash splash)   ripple lap course tour

7. (resilient strong)   (taxing demanding)   tough arduous stout stiff

8. (flatten demolish)   (rank standing)   ravage station total level

9. (peak top)   (fall topple)   crest apex tip tilt

10. (bulk capacity)   (book tome)   edition size amount volume

11. What is $5^2 - 4^2$?

12. Zubin uses 60 grams of sugar, 120 grams of butter and 180 grams of flour to make shortbread. What is the ratio of sugar to flour in the shortbread? Circle the correct option.

    A   1:2   **C**   1:3   **E**   2:3

    B   2:1   **D**   3:2

13. What is $^3/_{16} + ^3/_8$? Circle the correct option.

    A $^6/_{16}$ **C** $^6/_8$ **E** $^9/_8$

    B $^9/_{16}$ **D** $^6/_{24}$

14. The first four rectangles in a sequence are shown below.

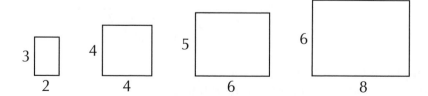

What is the area of the next rectangle in the sequence?

15. Which of the following shows the plan view of the 3D shape below?
Circle the correct option.

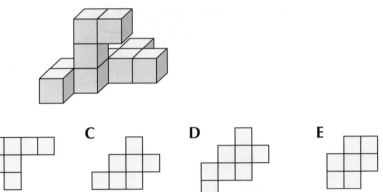

A   B   C   D   E

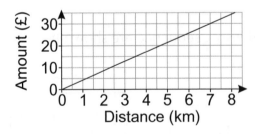

16. $32 \div 2a = 8$. What is the value of a?

17. Ivan and Karina are running in a sponsored charity event. The graph below shows how much money they raise, depending on how far they run.

Karina runs 12.3 km. Ivan raises £45.
How much further does Karina run than Ivan?

☐☐☐☐ m

/ 17

Q1-7 will test your **non-verbal reasoning** skills.
You have **4 minutes** to complete Q1-7.

Find the figure in each row that is most unlike the others.

1.

   a   b   c   d   e

2.

   a   b   c   d   e

3.

   a   b   c   d   e

4.

   a   b   c   d   e

5.

   a   b   c   d   e

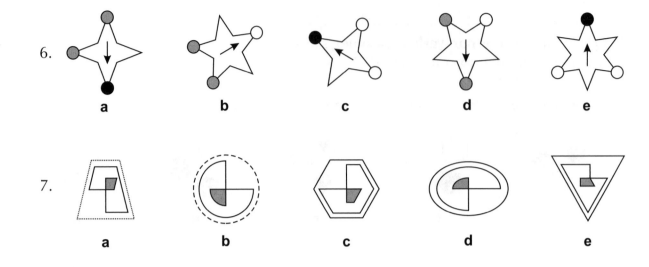

6.   a   b   c   d   e

7.   a   b   c   d   e

Q8-25 will test your **verbal reasoning** skills.
You have **6 minutes** to complete Q8-25.

In each question below, the words can be rearranged to form a sentence.
One word doesn't fit in the sentence. Underline the word that doesn't fit.

Example: red   the   has   <u>ride</u>   girl   bicycle   a

8.   her   weak   paper   incredibly   well   was   to   written   letter   the

9.   site   everyone   to   the   helmets   on   promised   mask   building   wear

10.   loud   up   my   wake   sirens   clock   enough   me   isn't   alarm   to

11.   younger   climbed   Katie's   was   Everest   he   failure   when   dad   Mount

12.   cheese   smelled   mouse   to   does   new   eat   our   pet   like   not

Three of the words in each list are linked. Mark the word that is not related to these three.

Example: journal   diary   <u>textbook</u>   notebook

13. lithe   sleek   silky   glossy

14. limp   hobble   stutter   shuffle

15. watch   spectacles   bracelet   bangle

16. recall   withdraw   decamp   retreat

17. wrinkle   crease   furrow   flush

18. rotate   pivot   alternate   swivel

Find the word that means the opposite, or nearly the opposite, of the word on the left.

Example: **first**   later   <u>last</u>   next   beginning

19. **lenient**   hateful   limited   temperate   severe

20. **noxious**   harmless   rejuvenating   righteous   gracious

21. **plunge**   advance   accelerate   ascend   immerse

22. **pride**   misery   humility   passivity   reticence

23. **deep**   pensive   superficial   profound   cursory

24. **official**   indecent   furtive   sanctioned   unauthorised

25. **deterioration**   alteration   regression   improvement   reawakening

/ 25

Puzzles 9

These puzzles are fantastic for practising your **vocabulary** and **problem-solving** skills.

Superior Synonyms

Romesh wants to use more exciting words to make his story more interesting. Fill in the gaps below to complete a synonym for each of the words in bold.

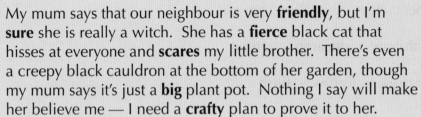

My mum says that our neighbour is very **friendly**, but I'm **sure** she is really a witch. She has a **fierce** black cat that hisses at everyone and **scares** my little brother. There's even a creepy black cauldron at the bottom of her garden, though my mum says it's just a **big** plant pot. Nothing I say will make her believe me — I need a **crafty** plan to prove it to her.

1. _ f f _ b _ _

2. _ _ n v i _ c _ _

3. f _ r _ c _ _ _ s

4. _ n t i _ i d _ t _ _ _

5. _ i _ a _ t _ c

6. _ u _ n i _ _

Mind the Cliff

Amy's hot air balloon is heading towards a cliff and is 50 m away. To get the balloon to rise, Amy can blast the burner, which makes the balloon rise by 13 m, or drop a ballast, which makes the balloon rise by 7 m.

- How can Amy make the balloon rise exactly 60 m using the burner and the ballasts?

- If the balloon travels 9 m forward every time the burner is used, how can Amy get over the height of the cliff by using only the burner?

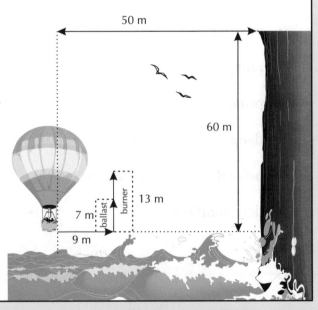

Q1-7 will test your **comprehension** skills.
You have **6 minutes** to complete Q1-7.

Read this passage carefully and answer the questions that follow.

The Brontë Sisters

Charlotte, Emily and Anne Brontë were three sisters who defied expectations for nineteenth-century women. Far from the literary circles of London, in the impoverished village of Haworth on the edge of some of Yorkshire's dramatic moorland, they wrote some of the most famous novels in the English language.

5   The sisters showed rich imagination from an early age and as children they created the elaborate fantasy worlds of 'Angria' and 'Gondal'. Their father, a clergyman, always encouraged his children's education, and they soon began writing their stories down. This sparked their ambition to become published authors.

Their love of writing continued into adulthood, and Charlotte was determined that
10   all three of them should get their work published. They successfully found a publisher for their joint book of poetry, which they published under names that disguised their female identity — Currer, Ellis and Acton Bell. These pseudonyms corresponded to the initials of their real names. In the nineteenth century, many people considered it inappropriate for women to make a living from writing, and the Brontës feared they
15   would face prejudice if their true identities were known.

Although their poetry only sold a handful of copies, the sisters were undeterred and strived to publish their novels. After Charlotte's first novel was rejected by publishers, 'Jane Eyre' went on to become an overwhelming success and established Charlotte as an important literary figure of her day. Some people were shocked by Emily's
20   'Wuthering Heights' because of the cruelty and violence it depicted. Similarly, Anne's 'The Tenant of Wildfell Hall' was controversial because of its harrowing themes. Today, the three women are renowned for their contribution to literature.

Answer these questions about the text that you've just read.
Circle the letter that matches the correct answer.

1. Which of the following best describes where the Brontës lived?

    A   An isolated cottage on the moors.

    B   A village on the outskirts of London.

    C   A deprived part of the country.

    D   On the border between Yorkshire and Derbyshire.

2. According to the text, what inspired the Brontës to pursue writing careers?

    A   Their father was an established author and poet.

    B   As children, they wrote stories about imaginary lands.

    C   They felt that education was very important.

    D   They found life in their village very boring.

3. Which of the following statements about Acton Bell is true?

    A   He is the youngest Brontë brother.

    B   It is the name of the publishing company that printed the sisters' poetry.

    C   It is the pen name of Anne Brontë.

    D   He is a fan of the Brontës' work.

4. Which of the following statements is true?

    A   Charlotte was jealous of Emily's poetry.

    B   The Brontës felt that writing was a childish pastime.

    C   The sisters thought that books by women were less likely to be published.

    D   Anne was reluctant to be published alongside her sisters.

5. Which of the following statements about the Brontës' careers must be false?

    A   The Brontës' collection of poetry was a commercial success.

    B   The sisters wrote prose as well as poems.

    C   Charlotte's work initially faced opposition from publishers.

    D   Charlotte was more famous than her sisters during her lifetime.

6. According to the text, what did Emily and Anne's novels have in common?

   A   They were lauded for their originality.

   B   They were criticised for using harsh language.

   C   They outsold Charlotte's 'Jane Eyre'.

   D   Their subject matter was considered inappropriate by some.

7. According to the text, which of the following
   statements about the Brontë sisters must be true?

   A   They overcame dire poverty.

   B   They behaved as women of their time were expected to.

   C   They were at the centre of London society.

   D   They produced influential works of literature.

Q8-12 will test your **maths** skills.
You have **4 minutes** to complete Q8-12.

8. Eleanor buys a mango for 80p using a £5 note. She is given her
   change as four pound coins and the rest in 5 pence pieces.
   How many 5 pence pieces does she receive?

9. Gerry cuts 9 equal lengths of wood from a 85 cm long plank.
   He has 4 cm left over. How long is each of the 9 lengths?

   cm

105   Workout 27

10. The diagram below shows a lake on a map. Each square of the grid is 1 km². Use the grid to estimate the area of the lake. Circle the correct option.

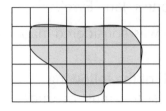

A 22 km²   **C** 25 km²   **E** 30 km²

B 18 km²   **D** 12 km²

11. Which of the following expression is incorrect? Circle the correct option.

A 11 × 11 = 47 + 74

B 7 × 12 = 14 × 6

C 144 ÷ 12 < 16 × 1.5

D $^{26}/_6 + {}^{10}/_6 > 50 ÷ 10$

E 160 − 79 = 41 × 2

12. Nestor rented a car for 5 days. The cost of renting the car in Euros is worked out using the expression $30d + 2m$, where d is the number of days and m is the number of miles over 500 driven during the rental period. Over the 5 days Nestor drove 576 miles. How much did renting the car cost him?

€

/ 12

Q1-5 will test your **maths** skills.
You have **4 minutes** to complete Q1-5.

1. Victor has 25 chocolates. Every day he eats three chocolates. After how many days will he have only one chocolate left? Circle the correct option.

    A 9   **C** 5   **E** 7

    B 8   **D** 10

2. The diagram shows a cross-section of a bath tub, which is a semicircle. How deep is the bath at its deepest point?

    0.8 m

    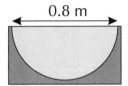

     cm

Uma recorded the number of emails she received each day for a week and the number of those which were advertising emails.

Day	Emails	Advertising Emails
Monday	25	15
Tuesday	21	
Wednesday	29	6
Thursday	18	10
Friday	34	21

3. Work out the percentage of the emails Uma received on Monday that were not advertising emails. Circle the correct option.

    A 80%   **C** 60%   **E** 70%

    B 20%   **D** 40%

4. The mean number of advertising emails Uma received per day was 12.2. How many advertising emails did Uma receive on Tuesday?

5. Donna has been on a ferris wheel for 4 minutes. The wheel takes 24 minutes to complete one full turn. How many more degrees from this point will the wheel turn through before Donna is back to where she got on?

Q6-16 will test your **non-verbal reasoning** skills.
You have **6 minutes** to complete Q6-16.

Work out which option would look like the figure on the left if it was rotated.

6. **Rotate**

                                   a   **b**   **c**   **d**

7. **Rotate**

                                   a   **b**   **c**   **d**

8. **Rotate**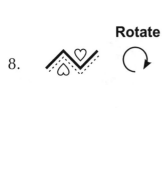

a   b   c   d

9. **Rotate**

a   b   c   d

10. **Rotate**

a   b   c   d

Look at how the first bug changes to become the second bug. Then work out which option would look like the third bug if you changed it in the same way.

11.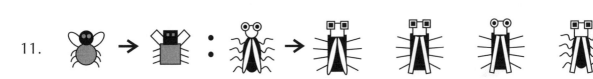

                                       a   b   c   d

12.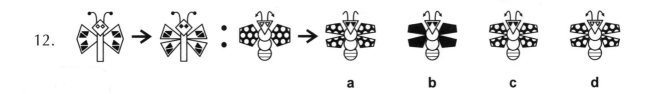

                                       a   b   c   d

Workout 28

13.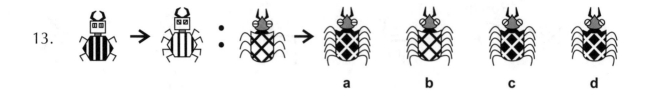

a b c d

Work out which of the options best fits in place of the missing hexagon in the grid.

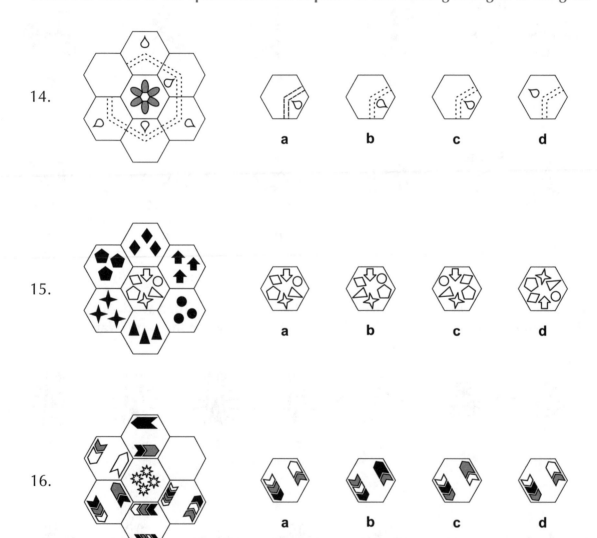

14.

a b c d

15.

a b c d

16.

a b c d

/ 16

Q1-7 will test your **comprehension** skills.
You have **6 minutes** to complete Q1-7.

Read this passage carefully and answer the questions that follow.

An abridged extract from 'A Study in Scarlet'

We met next day as he had arranged, and inspected the rooms at No. 221B, Baker Street. They consisted of a couple of comfortable bed-rooms and a single large airy sitting-room, cheerfully furnished, and illuminated by two broad windows. So desirable in every way were the apartments, and so moderate did the terms seem
5 when divided between us, that the bargain was concluded upon the spot, and we at once entered into possession. That very evening I moved my things round from the hotel, and on the following morning Sherlock Holmes followed me with several boxes and portmanteaus*. For a day or two we were busily employed in unpacking and laying out our property to the best advantage. That done, we gradually began to settle
10 down and to accommodate ourselves to our new surroundings.

Holmes was certainly not a difficult man to live with. He was quiet in his ways, and his habits were regular. It was rare for him to be up after ten at night, and he had invariably breakfasted and gone out before I rose in the morning. Sometimes he spent his day at the chemical laboratory, sometimes in the dissecting-rooms, and
15 occasionally in long walks, which appeared to take him into the lowest portions of the City**. Nothing could exceed his energy when the working fit was upon him; but now and again a reaction would seize him, and for days on end he would lie upon the sofa in the sitting-room, hardly uttering a word or moving a muscle from morning to night.

20 As the weeks went by, my interest in him and my curiosity as to his aims in life, gradually deepened and increased.

Arthur Conan Doyle

* portmanteaus — *suitcases*
** the City — *the City of London*

Answer these questions about the text that you've just read.
Circle the letter that matches the correct answer.

1. Which of the following best describes the sitting room?

   A   Dingy and uninviting

   B   Vast and lavish

   C   Comfortable and compact

   D   Bright and spacious

2. According to the text, which of the following statements must be true?

   A   The rent for the apartment is very reasonable.

   B   The apartment is close to John's hotel.

   C   John and Sherlock manage to negotiate a lower rent.

   D   Sherlock knows the owner of the apartment.

3. Which of the following words best describes how
   Sherlock and John behave in lines 1-6?

   A   Impatiently   C   Tentatively

   B   Decisively   D   Dutifully

4. Which of the following words best describes Sherlock in lines 11-13?

   A   Predictable

   B   Candid

   C   Cordial

   D   Erratic

5. What does the word "invariably" (line 13) mean?

   A   In a changeable manner

   B   In a strange manner

   C   In a consistent manner

   D   In an unpleasant manner

6. Which of the following best describes Sherlock's habits?

   A   He only frequents respectable parts of London.

   B   He spends most of his time resting.

   C   He is often out all night.

   D   He engages in scientific study.

7. According to the text, how does John feel about Sherlock?

   A   He thinks he and Sherlock are too different to live together.

   B   He admires Sherlock's lifestyle.

   C   He is intrigued by Sherlock.

   D   He thinks Sherlock is lazy.

Q8-12 will test your **maths** skills.
You have **4 minutes** to complete Q8-12.

8.   What is $0.5 \times 4691 \times 2$?

9.   Neville is putting paintbrushes into pots. Each pot can hold 11 brushes. How many pots will he need for 91 brushes?

10. An ice cube tray has 12 wells that make perfect identical cubes. Each well is 2 cm deep. What volume of water can the ice cube tray hold in total? Circle the correct option.

   A   100 cm³

   B   82 cm³

   C   96 cm³

   D   78 cm³

   E   50 cm³

Seren identified 72 flying insects that she found in her garden. Her results are shown in the pie chart below.

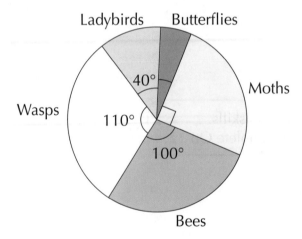

11. What fraction of the insects were either wasps or bees? Circle the correct option.

   A   ⁷/₁₂   **C**   ¹¹/₁₆   **E**   ⁶/₁₁

   B   ⁵/₆   **D**   ¹/₉

12. Half of the butterflies Seren identified were white. How many white butterflies did she identify?

/ 12

Q1-7 will test your **maths** skills.
You have **6 minutes** to complete Q1-7.

1. The clock below shows the time Harper arrived home one evening.
If it took her 1 hour and 35 minutes to get home, what time did she set off?

 : pm

2. A shop is having a 20% discount sale. Helle buys a towel in the sale for £8.
What was the price of the towel before the sale?

£

Gibran records the number of steps he takes each day:

7892, 12 098, 10 097, 11 204, 8981

3. What is the difference between the greatest and the fewest number of
steps taken by Gibran on a single day?

4. Use estimation to work out the mean number of steps Gibran took per
day. Circle the correct option.

    A 11 023.4   **C** 10 054.4   **E** 13 230.6

    B 88 701.2   **D** 6291.9

5. Rory is swimming lengths of a pool. His target is 8 lengths. Rory has swum
    four and a half lengths. How much of his target has he already completed?
    Circle the correct option.

    A $^1/_8$ **C** $^7/_{16}$ **E** $^9/_{16}$

    B $^3/_8$ **D** $^3/_5$

The rectangle show on the axes below has a width of 2 units and a height of 4 units.
Point *P* on the rectangle has the coordinates (*b*, 3).

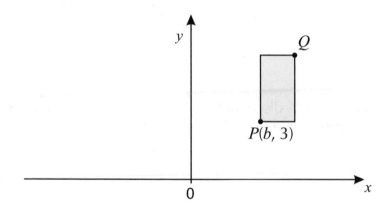

6. Which of the following describes the coordinates of point *Q*?
    Circle the correct option.

    A (2, 3)   **C** (2*b*, 3)   **E** (−*b* − 2, 7)

    B (−2, 3)   **D** (*b* + 2, 7)

7. The rectangle is moved so that the new coordinates of *P* are (−*b*, 2).
    Which of the following describes how the rectangle was moved?
    Circle the correct option.

    A 1 right and 3*b* up

    B *b* right and *b* up

    C 2*b* left and 1 down

    D 2*b* right and 2 up

    E 2 left and 2 up

**Look at how the first two figures are changed, and then work out which option would
look like the third figure if you changed it in the same way.**

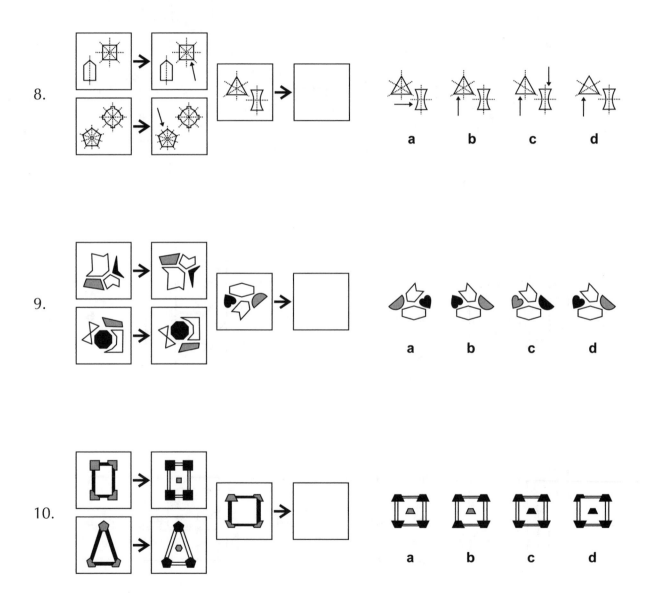

8.

     a   b   c   d

9.

     a   b   c   d

10.

     a   b   c   d

Work out which 3D figure in the grey box has been rotated to make the new 3D figure.

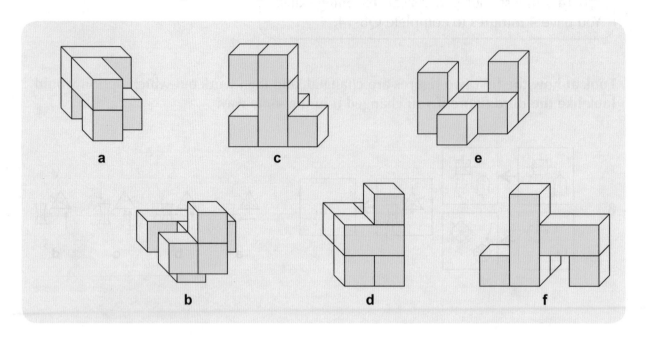

a

c

e

b

d

f

11.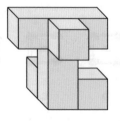

a	d
b	e
c	f

12.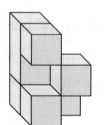

a	d
b	e
c	f

13.

a	d
b	e
c	f

14.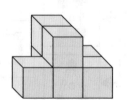

a	d
b	e
c	f

/ 14

L6XWDE2